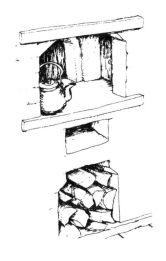

The Book of
Masonry Stoves

Rediscovering an
Old Way of Warming

The Book of

Masonry Stoves

Rediscovering an Old Way of Warming

David Lyle

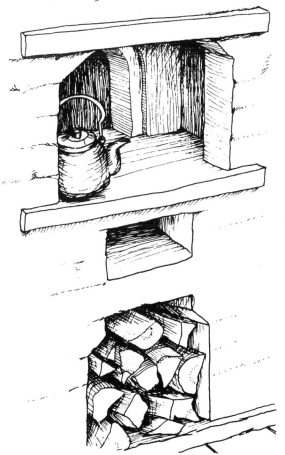

New Illustrations by
Nicholas Lyle & Kristin Musgnug

CHELSEA GREEN PUBLISHING COMPANY   White River Junction, Vermont

Illustrations: Nicholas Lyle and Kristen Musgnug (new illustrations except where noted on artwork)
Book design: Wilson Graphics & Design (Kenneth J. Wilson)

Originally published by Brick House Publishing Co., Inc.
First Chelsea Green printing September, 1997.

Printed in the United States of America
8 7 6 5   05 06 07 08

Library of Congress Cataloging in Publication Data

Lyle, David.
    The book of masonry stoves.

    Bibliography: p. 179
    Includes index.
    1. Stoves, Masonry. I. Title.
TH7436.M37L94 1983 683.´.88 83-3897
ISBN 1-890132-09-8 (pbk.)

CHELSEA GREEN PUBLISHING COMPANY
P.O. Box 428
White River Junction, Vermont 05001
(800) 639-4099
www.chelseagreen.com

Figure 1 A man warming himself before
the fire in medieval England. The illustration
is from a drawing in an old manuscript.

*The late emperor Francis wittily observed
one day, that he believed "it required as much talent
to warm a room, as to rule a kingdom," and I really
think he was not far from the truth.*

John Paget,
Hungary and Transylvania,
Philadelphia, 1850.

Dedicated with love and gratitude to my companions and guides on this road.

Acknowledgments

Eight years ago when the idea for this book first occurred to me, I went in search of other books on the subject. The first place I looked for references was in the bibliography of *The City in History* by Lewis Mumford. There I found the following entry: "Meikelham, Robert. *On the History and Art of Warming and Ventilating Rooms and Buildings.* 2 vols. London: 1845. Important: a rare book in a poorly explored field. Needs an even more exhaustive successor." That told me what I suspected and needed to know, and so in a way it is thanks to Lewis Mumford that this book was written, though his plea for a more exhaustive successor remains unanswered.

Many have helped me, some directly, others through the records they left in books and journals, some of them very old. To all I am profoundly grateful. For errors and omissions bound to appear in a work of this kind, I am of course solely responsible.

Much of the lore of stove building is not available in books. Two master stove builders from Austria, Gustav Jung and Josef Thurner, have very generously offered a great deal of technical information based on their own experience. So has the Swedish master stove builder Mats Lindholm, and from Finland Kari Mäkelä. I owe special thanks to two people without whom this book, in its present form, could not have been written: to Helen Frink, for her many careful translations from German and French, which made a great amount of valuable material accessible to me; and to Björn-Erik Lindblom of Sweden, whose translations, research, and knowledge of tile stoves have been invaluable. I am especially indebted to Catherine Perlès of the University of Paris for her help with the use of fire in prehistory, and to Theodore A. Wertime of the Smithsonian, for guidance on early pyrotechnology in the Middle East. I am indebted to Dr. Jurgis

Gimbutas for translations from his father's book and for advice on Lithuanian stoves, and also to Prof. Ildikó Kríza-Horváth for help with material from Hungary. I am grateful to Prof. Hans Reinerth for his advice on prehistoric hearths; to Pauls Kundzins for advice on Latvia and the east Baltic; to Prof. Ronald F. Tylecote of the University of London for advice on early furnaces, kilns, and ovens. Mrs. Pat Carter, of Baker Library at Dartmouth College, has found the unfindable for me in the realm of books. Anne O'Dowd of the National Museum of Ireland has also been very helpful.

Edward W. Poitras of Seoul offered much assistance with the Korean *ondol*, as did Dr. Dietwulf Baatz of the Saalburg on the Roman hypocaust. I have Tony Rook of England to thank on hypocausts as well, and Louis Dupree for what information I have been able to find on the *tawakhaneh*. For their personal interest and care with translations I wish to thank Patrick A. O'Sullivan, Olga Bassinne, Signe Motter, Kazys Daugela, Suki Choe, Marianne Kahn, Eva Horton, Karen Getty, and Majlen Helenius. Prof. Marija Gimbutas has offered helpful advice on ovens; William R. Greer has been unstinting in his aid on the same subject. For enlightening discussion on wood burning I owe thanks to Walter Goodridge, president of Tekton Corp., Conway, Massachusetts; Walter Lange, head of L. Lange & Co., Svendborg, Denmark; Garlan Hoskin, of Svendborg Co., Hanover, New Hampshire; to Prof. Richard C. Hill of the University of Maine; and to Heinz and Peter Schweizer of the Tiba Co., stove makers of Bubendorf, Switzerland.

I owe particular thanks to Audrey Lyle for listening to endless stove discussions, for taking over tasks that made it possible for me to work on this book, for reading the manuscript, and for offering helpful suggestions. Nicholas Lyle, my son, and Kristin Musgnug prepared at top speed a great many of the illustrations that I believe contribute so much to this book; I'm very grateful for the care and dedication with which they did this. I owe much, too, to some companions: the Warehouse Irregulars, Audrey, Ben, Chops, Jenny, Nick, Purly, Berny, and Gaale; and of course Katy, Jessie, and Madeleine. My special thanks to Alice E. Brown for her care in typing the manuscript and for her faith in its virtues.

Contents

Why Masonry Stoves?

If this book has any single goal, it is to encourage new attitudes toward wood burning in North America.

We are accustomed to iron stoves. That is our tradition. Elsewhere in the world, many prefer masonry. So let me begin by listing some of the virtues that well-designed masonry stoves and fireplace-stoves may have:

- They are substantially more efficient than the typical iron stoves on the market today.

- They are safer to live with than iron stoves.

- They can sharply reduce air pollution from smoke.

- They fit in well with solar heating. The same heat-storage system—rock, brick, or water—can serve both.

- Masonry stoves require fuel only once or twice a day.

- They do not parch the room air and so are more comfortable to live with than iron models.

- They offer design flexibility impossible with iron; the masonry stove can be designed to fit the house.

Some provisos go with these claims: The stove must be correctly designed; it must be built with care; it must be operated as intended. But these are not impossible standards. Tens of thousands of new masonry stoves meet them every year in Europe.

What about cost? Masonry stoves that will heat a house are already being built in North America for $2,200 to $3,500 and up. In my area that's about the price of a traditional masonry fireplace, and it is less than the installed cost of a typical central heating system. Prefabrication of masonry stove components, now commencing in the U.S., may cut costs even more, and perhaps by a lot more. Stoves in the $1,000 to $2,000 range may be possible; time will tell. (Note: By "masonry stove" I mean both closed stoves and those heat storage stoves run with doors open, like fireplaces.)

Recently someone prominent in the iron stove world asked why I was looking into the past, at masonry stoves, for answers to wood-burning questions in the twentieth century. The answers, the expert said, would come from space-age technology. Period.

Faith in the technical fix is seductive. And who would deny the marvels wrought in our own time by space-age technicians? Still it hasn't always gone well. For reasons unclear to me but no doubt compelling, the national space agency for years sponsored efforts to track a turtle through water; all were unsuccessful.* So it goes in mundane affairs. Even as we accomplish miracles in space, the parlor stove smokes and turtles wander untracked through the seas. In the United States wood provides more energy than nuclear power. Still the big money goes to matters atomic; we are left to find our own way in warming the parlor with wood. Perhaps it is just as well. It seems worthwhile to value self-reliance in such matters, rather than to await experts.

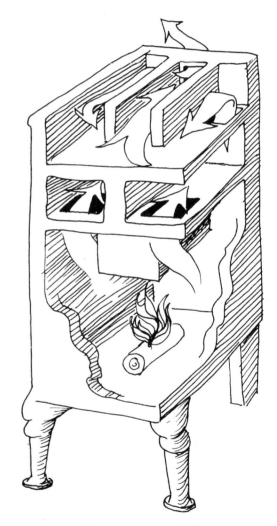

Figure 2 This small central European tile stove would be used to warm a single room.

---

*For the record of the effort, see Harold T. P. Hayes's excellent book, *Three Levels of Time*.

Historians know the past may hold answers, if one can get at them. Not much attention has been paid to this in recent times, at least as regards wood burning. Our ancestors knew a lot. We descend from generation after generation of wood burners. Over thousands of years humans have shown mind-boggling ingenuity in consuming wood by fire. Ideas being put forward today as new, the hot concepts of an enlightened stove industry, were in fact known during the Stone Age. Stoves sold today as "the latest" and "the best" lack the sophistication of others built two centuries ago and more.

As to the present value of old technology in stoves, look for a moment at Finland. Finland is an advanced country, known for fine workmanship and good design. The Finns are international traders. Their products have to be good, especially in regard to heating because their climate is like that of Alaska. Today Finland's government actively encourages the construction of masonry stoves through tax policy. About two-thirds of Finland's new houses have built-in masonry stoves; most of the rest have wood-fired masonry baking ovens which can also be used for space heating. This government policy says a good deal about Finland's confidence in an old technology, even in the space age. It says something as well about the country's assessment of the energy situation.

Why do masonry stoves remain little known in North America? A reasonable question, to which there are answers both cultural and historical; I'll get to them in chapter 2. Meantime, consider the following:

In the colder areas of Europe and Asia (including Siberia and Manchuria) masonry heating systems were far more common during the wood-burning era than were iron stoves. Korea, north China, Russia, Finland, Sweden, Lithuania, Estonia, Latvia, Poland, Hungary, Rumania, Yugoslavia, Austria, Switzerland, much of Germany—in all of these countries masonry stoves were the common type. When I learned this, my first skeptical thought was that masonry is an older building material than iron. People built masonry stoves originally because they could get clay and stone for nothing. Iron cost money. The cultural tradition of masonry had simply hung on until modern times.

This is true, but it is a limited truth.

Figure 3 The massive Russo-Finnish type of masonry stove would be the sole source of warmth for a dwelling.

Low-cost iron stoves became widely available long ago. In the traditional lands of the masonry stove they were tried out as elsewhere. But the iron stove was considered second-rate, something to be relegated to peripheral areas of life. The authors of an old Russian encyclopedia (the *Entsiklopedicheskij slovar*, St. Petersburg, 1898) expressed themselves in a typical way. They found the iron stove suitable only for warm climates, or for heating rooms that could be allowed to grow cold at night. In Russia at that period, they reported, iron stoves were used only to heat shops or work places, plus the occasional living space where nothing else would fit. The authors of the article happened to be Russians. They could as well have been Austrians or Swedes or Finns. All found the iron stove sometimes useful, but clearly inferior to the masonry model.

Some years ago, as I looked into the various traditional methods of wood burning around the world, the depth of feeling among masonry stove partisans began to come home to me. They did not simply feel that masonry stoves were better; they felt that, given an opportunity for choice, *no other choice could be made!* At this point, rather like the mule struck by the baseball bat to get his attention, I began to feel that there might be a message here for North America. The farther I looked, the more relevant the message seemed. Masonry stoves were superior in a number of ways. They were not without shortcomings. Nor were iron stoves simply to be cast aside—they have their own virtues, sometimes very considerable ones. But as the momentum of wood burning increased in North America, the logic of masonry stoves and fireplace-stoves seemed ever more apparent. They offered a superior approach to wood burning, and I felt it ought to become much more widely known.

Recent surveys suggest that at least twelve to fifteen million wood stoves are now in use in the United States. More are being added every day. As this movement continues, the logic of masonry stove use should become dramatically more apparent. Because this notion will seem unfamiliar to many readers, it seems worthwhile to discuss it briefly before going on.

When interest in wood burning began to reawaken in 1974 with the oil crisis, it was largely on a no-questions-asked basis. Wood burning was widely seen without reservations as a "good" thing. As a wood burner you cut down on oil use, thwarted OPEC, saved money, became more self-reliant. You used a "renewable resource," in the jargon of the day. Maybe you even hung out a bumper sticker that said "Split Wood Not Atoms." Evangelistic fervor is likely to be part of any shift in social directions; certainly it often is in America, and I'm not knocking it. Where wood burning is concerned, I've traveled that road myself. But there always comes a time of questioning, when fervor is no longer enough. And that time has come. Wood burning is no longer an unequivocally "good" thing. Problems are arising. To anyone with a knowledge of history, this will come as no surprise. There were problems in the past in plenty.

As the return to wood burning began after 1974, the press tended to focus on success stories. Usually these were about the citizen who installed a new stove, burned five cords of wood cut from his own land, and reduced his annual oil bill to $22.50. There were a lot of those stories, and they were genuine. But such stories are mostly gone now. People still cut the oil bill by burning wood. But the story is old hat. It is no longer news. Something else is in the wind.

The *New York Times* and the *Wall Street Journal* have both carried front-page stories about the dangers of air pollution from wood burning. Regional papers have picked up the same story. The Environmental Protection Agency has begun to look into it. In our society, which tends to measure everything, statistics have begun to emerge. Oregon's Department of Environmental Quality said up to 78 percent of air pollution in some towns comes from wood smoke. A researcher reported that Portland, Oregon has *more emissions from residential wood heating than from all industry combined.* Some sixty-five hundred tons of particulate fallout descend on the city each year from its wood stoves and fireplaces, a kind of ash rain. There is perhaps ten times more fine fallout drifting down,

Figure 4 Air pollution from wood burning was once common. Note the absence of chimneys in this eighteenth-century French glassworks.

What we will stand for remains to be seen, but the pollution question is coming to the fore. Some components of wood smoke are demonstrably bad to breathe. Movements to restrict pollution from wood burning are already underway in Oregon, Colorado and Montana. Once it is understood that air pollution need not follow from the use of wood stoves, more may be done about it elsewhere. One answer is the masonry stove; it can burn cleanly. In the process, it can also burn safely and with high efficiency. Not a bad bargain. More about efficiency in a later chapter; let's consider safety.

In my own New England town, perhaps 80 percent of the residential fire calls answered by our volunteer fire company are related to wood-stove use. It is a rural town and wood stoves are common. Chimney fires are the most frequent source of trouble. Creosote builds up; then it catches fire. Next come poorly installed stoves: Something overheats and the house catches fire. It's an old problem, one we've tended to forget. Many people install their own stoves today, and believe they know what they are about. The fact that they don't know may come to light only years later, when a fire starts inside a wall.

A year or two back, the *New York Times* ran another front-page story, this one about the increase in accidental fires from wood stove use. I believe the possibility of such fires is sitting out there like a time bomb waiting to happen. We are

fallout below the official particulate level in size. "We have," said the researcher, "a tremendous problem in some of our air sheds."

Reading about Oregon's air, I recalled a conversation I had a few years ago with the head of a stove company in Switzerland. "Do you really think," he asked, "that iron stoves will come into general use in America? What about air pollution?" I had no reply ready. The question wasn't being asked then in America. I simply said that iron stoves were, whatever the consequences, coming into wide use. "In Switzerland," he said, "I don't believe the country would stand for the kind of air pollution you're likely to get."

Figure 5 Thatch, once widely used as a roofing material, was a major fire risk because of sparks from the wood fire. Ladders were often kept at hand so the householder could dash up and douse the fire in the roofing. In this Japanese dwelling, the Chinese character for water has been worked into the gable end in the hope that it will protect the house.

curiously inattentive to such things in the United States. America has by a vast margin the highest death rate by fire among all industrialized countries in the world. Yet this fact somehow escapes attention. The return to wood burning, with our present low safety standards, may bring change.

Masonry stoves can sharply reduce wood-burning safety problems. The iron stove is frequently so hot that it will burn anyone who touches it. The masonry stove is commonly designed in Europe with benches attached, so that you can sit and lean against the stove. There is a world of difference in safety between a stove you can lean on and one that burns at the touch. In eastern and central Europe, people slept on the traditional masonry stove. So did the Chi-

nese. The chances of getting a burn from such a stove, or of setting fire to anything close to it, are much diminished if not eliminated.

There is another safety factor. *Correctly designed and used, a masonry stove will produce no creosote buildup in the chimney.* The chimney flue above a masonry stove should never require cleaning, ever. Unless birds nest in it. So the risk of chimney fire is eliminated. With a masonry stove, the idea is to achieve complete combustion; if you do that, no soot or creosote can form. The effects are twofold: higher efficiency and the elimination of soot-clogged chimneys, not to mention the elimination of those little items that escape the chimney and become air pollution.

Today safety, as well as air pollution and the related factor of low efficiency, are becoming central questions in wood burning. The problems are real; but they are just beginning to be recognized. I believe masonry stove technology offers answers to these problems, and that is one of the major messages of this book. Some of the other virtues of the masonry stove—comfort, convenience, design flexibility, and compatibility with solar heating—are at least equally real and worthwhile. These qualities are discussed in later chapters.

Perhaps it is best now to say a word about what the reader may expect. The book is addressed to all who burn wood, with the thought that some may wish to consider a masonry stove. Part I pro-

vides a historical perspective on wood burning. Part II covers the major types of masonry heating systems as they have evolved mainly over the past four hundred years and as they exist today. Part III is addressed primarily to the mason, designer, or builder; it attends to technical and construction details.

Now let me add a word of caution. When I began looking into the masonry stove world, there seemed two possible courses. One was to start building stoves and testing them. Another was to research what others had done and *then* start building. I took the second path. Thus I have not built, or compared through use, the many stove designs illustrated in these pages. In fact, no one has. Research comparing one type of masonry stove with the next, over the vast region where they are used, has never been undertaken. So what you will find here is a report. It describes what I have seen, heard, and read in several countries. I have made an effort to be accurate. I have tried to cross-check information with others, and against my own fifteen years' experience in using many types of iron stoves. But in the world of masonry stoves, information is seldom written down. Facts can be hard to come by, and differences of opinion and interpretation arise.

Given this context, I cannot guarantee the designs shown here on the basis of personal experience; I am passing on the word of others. It is necessary to say this because we live in a time when many

WHY MASONRY STOVES? 7

seek guarantees and assurances against every risk—death, taxes, and the possible treachery of appliances or bathmats. I cannot offer such guarantees. I *can* say that those who use masonry stoves abroad, including many shown here, have used them for centuries and continue to be devoted to them. I believe a similar regard can develop in North America. If, then, you wish to have a masonry stove today in North America, be advised: In Europe, a good designer will tell you that the stove should be fitted to the house, designed for specific needs and circumstances. That should be the path here, as it should be for any sort of heating equipment. I do not recommend that the inexperienced build stoves solely on the basis of designs shown in this book. Instead seek advice from those familiar with high temperature masonry construction, flue design, and refractory materials. Seek advice from someone who is familiar with your particular house and situation. The number of masons and companies with masonry stove experience is growing; sources of information are provided at the back of the book.

Finally, at an early stage I ceased to think of the stoves shown here as models for American masons to copy. Rather they represent a reservoir of knowledge, a knowledge of the trials, errors and occasional triumphs of the past. I've tried to describe what has gone before so that the shape of that reservoir becomes clear, and so that what has gone before

need not be reinvented. But my hope is that others will use this knowledge to develop new designs and not to copy old ones. European designs must be modified to fit North America; I strongly believe this is the right path to take. We need designs suited to our living and working habits, our fuels, housing and climates. Especially we need designs suited to the skills and experience of our masons, and to the materials they have available. We need designs moderate in cost and perhaps in part prefabricated. We need designs that use modern refractory materials and techniques. Perhaps above all we need designs that are safe.

At present in North America, the development of masonry stoves is about at the same stage solar heating reached a decade ago. That is, just beginning. The other day a hard-headed type from the building industry—not the solar industry, mind you, but the building industry—made a prediction. He said that by the mid 1980s, five hundred thousand houses a year would use passive solar designs. That represents 25 to 50 percent of the houses likely to be built in any given year. The masonry stove, or the fireplace/stove that uses masonry heat storage techniques, is the natural complement to passive solar designs. The process of developing the necessary stove designs has already begun. A favorable government tax policy, as in Finland, could encourage the process. It could also lead to safer and cleaner wood burning for millions of Americans.

In what follows, the terms central and eastern Europe are used in a somewhat unconventional manner. This is for convenience in defining certain styles of stove design. By central Europe I mean in the main the German-speaking regions—Switzerland, Austria, and Germany. By eastern Europe I mean primarily the U.S.S.R., Poland, Hungary, Rumania and the east Baltic countries, Estonia, Lithuania, Latvia; all have traditional stove designs that appear to be closely related. Finland appears to derive its more advanced stove designs from Swedish models, but Finland's traditional stoves are of an east European type. The west European countries such as France and Britain tended to use fireplaces or braziers, as did southern countries like Italy and Greece.

Conversion tables are provided in Appendix 1 for those who wish to convert metric measures into their U.S. equivalent, or vice versa.

PART 1
HISTORY

I sow ashes in the wind:
May evil omens melt like salt,
be lost like ashes in the wind.

Song of the Mnong Gar,
Men of the Forest,
upon burning wood-
lands to plant crops.*

*Excerpt from *We Have Eaten the Forest* by Georges Condominas,
translated by Adrienne Foulke. English translation
copyright © 1977 by Farrar, Straus and Giroux, Inc.
Reprinted by permission of Hill and Wang,
a division of Farrar, Straus and Giroux, Inc.

Chapter
1
Fire

This is the fire that will help the generations
to come, if they use it in a sacred manner. But if they do
not use it well, the fire will have the power to do them
great harm.

The Sacred Pipe*

*From *The Sacred Pipe: Black Elk's Account
of the Seven Rites of the Oglala Sioux.*
Recorded and Edited by Joseph Epes Brown.
Copyright 1953 by the University of Oklahoma Press.

In 1981 a group exploring the margin of what was probably an ancient lake in Kenya made a most unusual discovery. They had been searching for signs of early human habitation, and they found them, at a site that proved to be 1.4 million years old. Now this in itself was not remarkable; earlier sites are known. A mix of stone tools, nearly one thousand of them, marked the site. These were mingled with the fossil bones of hippopotamus, crocodile, antelope, and other animals; again interesting, but not unexpected.

The odd factor at the site was this: Mingled quite thoroughly with the bones and the stone tools were forty pieces of hard, "burnt clay." The largest pieces were two to three inches across. The scientists who discovered these burned shards see them as strong evidence for the earliest controlled use of fire by man. Presumably the clay underlaid the hearth and was hardened there by chance rather than design. One of our ancestors, *Homo erectus,* roamed Africa at the time; very likely he made the tools and kept the fire. It is possible that the maker of the tools was not responsible for the fire, that it had some other, perhaps accidental, source. But those who discovered the site believe the odds are against this. The close mingling of bones, tools, and fire-hardened clay strongly suggests a human agency at work, a hearth. If this is correct, then the earliest known human use of fire has been pushed back by almost a million years. The oldest hearths previously discovered—also the work of *Homo erectus*—were in southern France, Hungary, and China, but they dated back no more than five hundred thousand years.

The age of the Kenyan hearth is only one of two remarkable things about it.

Figure 6 The discovery of fire as visualized by Vitruvius. From an illustration of his work done in Nürnberg in 1548. Courtesy of the New York Public Library, Astor, Lenox and Tilden Foundations, Spencer Collection.

The other is its location in Africa. The evidence had previously suggested that fire first came into use in Europe and Asia, where it was colder and where (presumably for this reason) it was needed. But the cold theory seems defunct; cold was not a threat to our ancestors in Africa. So how had they come to use fire? What was its role in their lives? Fire of course has other charms, for cooking, for hardening wooden spear points, for working stone, and so on. For the moment, however, we have no certain answers, just the knowledge that our ancestor *Homo erectus* probably knew and used fire a very long time ago, along the margins of a vanished lake set about with crocodiles and hippos, at a time when energy for warmth was not a matter for human concern.

Somehow, perhaps because of the Prometheus legend, most of us come away from school with the notion that our own kind, *Homo sapiens,* discovered fire. But it didn't happen that way. Neanderthals had fire before us, and *Homo erectus* before that. Where fire is concerned we are not inventors but inheritors, inheritors of an ancient force that has shaped the life of our species since its first appearance on earth, and that shapes it still. Fire is at the heart of human life and history. We use it to form and reform our world, and it in turn expands and circumscribes our lives; we are married to fire as to no other force in nature. Just try to imagine human life without cooking, metals, concrete, glass, ceramics, or the stove's warmth on a winter night.

Carl Sauer, the American geographer, defined speech, tools, and fire as the tripod upon which all human culture rests. There are those who believe, though we lack and may never have the evidence to prove it, that the use of fire is older than the use of tools. The point is moot: Tools and fire have gone together among humankind since long before the appearance of our own species on earth. Without either, we would not remotely resemble the species we have become. As to speech, who can say? Fire has always been a focus for the group, especially at night. Gatherings around the fire are social occasions for talk, telling stories, passing on myth and knowledge. Such gatherings—and thus also fire—may have played a role in the extension of language.

Fire kept predators at a distance. Women with small children could remain safely in camp while men began to hunt in larger groups, relieved to some degree of a protective role. The hunting group learned to use fire to drive game and to kill it. Ancient hunters seem also to have used fire as a technique of game management, with lasting effect on the earth. Carl Sauer and others believe that repeated burning by man greatly enlarged the grasslands of North America and other regions, and that without this repeated burning, large areas of prairie would long ago have returned to forest. The vast pine forests of the southern United States are also a product of repeated burning, and not of the natural forest succession. Today we try to prevent forest fires because timber is economically important. Early man fostered fire all over the globe because open or semi-open land supports more game than does woodland. And game, not lumber, has been more important to humanity for more than 99 percent of its existence.

Recent experiments at the Land Institute in Salina, Kansas, suggest there may have been more to burning than merely keeping land open. Livestock at Salina were turned loose on grassland that had been prepared in various ways: by plowing, by harrowing only, by burning, and so on. The stock went straight to the areas that had been burned and ignored grass on the other plots.

With the development of agriculture about ten thousand years ago—quite recently in terms of three to four million years of human history—there came the practice of burning forest to create field. Ireland was once covered by forest. By the seventeenth century the forest had been destroyed and timber was imported. The same pattern was repeated in many parts of the earth: The cedars of Lebanon disappeared into countless ships now gone, just as today the redwoods disappear into ski chalets, hot tubs, and other fashions of the moment.

Regions still remain where nomadic farmers practice slash-and-burn agriculture, burning and planting patches of forest, then moving on after the field's fertility declines. After a decade or two the land may have recovered its productivity, and it will be cut and burned again for planting. In highland Vietnam the Mnong Gar—Men of the Forest—note the passage of time only by the burning of woodland to create fields for planting. "That was the year," they say, "when we ate the forest of the Stone Spirit." Georges Condominas, who studied and wrote about the Mnong Gar, recorded their chant as they burned the woodlands: "I fell the tree, doing as did the Ancestors; I clear the forest and the bush, doing as did the Ancestors . . ."* In such ways, burning to encourage game, clearing and burning to make fields, we have transformed the surface of the earth over tens and probably hundreds of thousands of years, turning woodland into grassland and, sometimes, into desert.

FIRE MAGIC AND FIRE LEGEND

At some point in the remote past fire became a focus of human magical and religious forms. There are even hints that fascination with fire extends beyond our own kind, far back into the history of ancestral species. Kenneth Oakley, a British

---

*Excerpt from *We Have Eaten the Forest* by George Condominas, translated by Adrienne Foulke. English translation copyright © 1977 by Farrar, Straus and Giroux, Inc. Reprinted by permission of Hill and Wang, a division of Farrar, Straus and Giroux, Inc.

scientist and one of the foremost authorities on the early use of fire, has remarked on the "deep subconscious or sensual appeal" of fire and suggested that this is a characteristic that we may share with other primates. One primate, the Philippine tarsier, was named *Tarsius carbonarus* because of a habit of picking up hot embers from campfire sites. This suggested to Oakley that "man's prehuman ancestors may have been attracted to natural fires and toyed with burning matter." It was not the first observation of the kind. Walter Hough of the Smithsonian has found a curious bit of lore in the writings of Samuel Purchas, an English compiler of travel books, who in 1619 said as follows: "The people of the countrie, when they travaile in the woods make fire when they sleep in the night; and in the morning when they are gone the Pongoes [apes] will come and

Figure 7 Fire seems always to have held a powerful attraction for man. This gathering at the fire appears in a medieval manuscript.

sit about the fire till it goeth out; for they have no understanding to lay the wood together."

Fire seems always to have held a fascination for humans. Our ancestors surrounded it with myth and ritual. Today we still make fire the focus of the living room whenever possible. Even the words connected with fire suggest its importance as a center, a focus of life. The word *focus* comes from a Latin word which originally meant hearth. The French word *foyer* means fireplace; figuratively it also means home. Very early in human history, then, home became the place that sheltered the fire.

Fire freed humans in the sense of permitting them to live more comfortably in cold regions, eat foods inedible without cooking, and enjoy protection from predators. But fire also bound them. As Alexander Marschak wrote in *The Roots of Civilization*, fire "must be tended; it needs a home and place out of the great winds, the heavy rains, the deepest snows; it must be constantly fed." From this a process evolves involving not just one person but the group, and the process shapes the group; it shapes the day, the pattern of life, the culture. Fuel must be found. Camps must be near fuel. If fuel runs low camps must be moved. Fire must be contained, fed, sheltered, watched. Not least the fire spirit must be treated correctly lest it become dangerous, as the Sioux and many other peoples believed.

All of this takes time and effort, and we are bound by that effort today as in the past, though perhaps, until the recent oil difficulties, it was easier to ignore that fact. In our economy of abundance fire is at the heart of the magic—in industrial plants, in automobiles, in homes. A fuel cutoff sends shocks through the entire world economy. Whole societies become uneasy, unstable, and there is a search for relief, for new ways to feed the flame and keep it burning.

All over the world gods, goddesses, spirits, and various rites have been associated with fire. This is only natural for a force that lies at the center of human life. The universality of the myths suggests that fire has been held sacred from very remote times. In Mexico a Nahuatl Indian prayer speaks of the fire god as the father and mother of gods, the most ancient divinity. In early human society, as the historian of religion Mircea Eliade has written, the shaman interceded with the powers of the natural world on his own and others' behalf, and he was often known as the "master of fire." Fire is a force not only powerful and difficult but also ambiguous, helpful and at the same time threatening; the shaman knew how to cope. Humans all seem to recognize the ambiguous nature of fire. The Egyptians expressed it in their many names for fire: The Useful One, The Executioner, The Living One, The Angry One, The Beautiful One, The Withering

One. Fire is a force to arouse awe; powerful, uncertain, and demanding special treatment to ensure safety. The rituals surrounding fire seem to go very far back. Neanderthals built fires over the graves of their dead.

Legends suggest where man first obtained fire and a good many speak of theft. The Polynesian hero Maui took fire from the volcano home of the fire god Mahuika. Coyote the Trickster stole fire for the Indians from the hearth of the Fire People. The best-known Western fire-giver was of course Prometheus. As Hesiod wrote, Prometheus "stole the radiant light of all-consuming fire in a hollow stalk" and gave it to man, in defiance of the gods.

One legend says Prometheus first gave fire to the people of the Greek island of Symi near the coast of Asia Minor. William Travis remarked a few years ago that shepherds on the island still carry fire by packing coals in the hollow stalk of the giant fennel, the same container Prometheus seems to have used. In his book, *Interval on Symi*, Travis suggested that Prometheus was an ordinary mortal from Asia Minor who somehow came to Symi by boat from the east, the direction of the sun, bearing fire in a hollow stalk and bringing it to the island for the first time.

The old stories suggest that in a time before humans knew how to make fire, they had to take it where they could find it. They had to approach a volcano or a forest fire, steal from the gods if need be, and at the risk of punishment. Fire gained at risk of course had to be guarded with care, and the role of fire-bringer or keeper arose. It may have been the first such specialized role in human society. It is certainly true that those able to deal with fire—the shaman and later the smith—had a special place and were set apart in society.

With the need to maintain fire came the tradition of the eternal flame, the fire never permitted to die. It was usually the women of the group who maintained it, as with the vestal virgins of ancient Rome at their temple. The tradition continues today with the Olympic torch, or the eternal flame at Arlington National Cemetery. Until quite recent times the Celtic peoples of Scotland, Ireland, and Wales maintained perpetual fires on their hearths. So long as a homestead was occupied, the fire was to be kept burning. There are reports of hearth fires burning for two and three hundred years. In Iran, where fire is central to the ancient Zoroastrian religion, there is a temple fire said to have burned continuously for twenty-five hundred years.

Figure 8 It remains uncertain whether fire was first made by striking sparks from stone, or by friction between two pieces of wood. This stylized drawing from an ancient Mexican manuscript illustrates the twirled stick method.

Keeping the Home Fires Burning

In most parts of Ireland the traditional fuel is turf. This meant long days in the bog harvesting the year's supply. Every sod of turf was handled many times, in cutting and spreading and footing, in drawing out and loading and unloading and ricking and clamping, and finally in keeping the fire built up to just the right degree needed for whatever was being done. In fine weather the work in the bog was pleasant enough, but if the early summer came bad it could be heartbreaking. In most houses the turf fire was kept alive under the ashes all night and revived again first thing in the morning. It might burn in this way for long years. Recently an old woman in County Limerick expressed her one regret on moving into a fine new house—the fire that had burned continuously on the old hearth for three hundred and thirty years was now gone out forever.

Kevin Danaher, *In Ireland Long Ago*, Mercier Press, Dublin, 1978.

NEEDFIRE AND BONFIRE

People of the past divided fire into different types, as Eskimos have names for dozens of snow types. *Wildfire* is a word that remains with us; others like *needfire, new fire,* and *strange fire* are rarely heard today. Strange fire was fire that violated certain rules for purity. Fire stolen from a family hearth is of this type, according to the anthropologist Walter Hough, as it becomes the means of using witchcraft against the family. The Bible records that Nadab and Abihu, the sons of Aaron, "offered strange fire before the Lord" in their censers, "And there went out fire from the Lord, and devoured them, and they died before the Lord."

Some years ago many American Indians began to follow the Ghost Dance religion, seeking among other things a return to some of the older, traditional ways. Followers were asked to abandon "the white man's flint and steel" and make fires by rubbing sticks together, as in the past. Ghost Dance followers were supposed to keep fires burning always in their lodges as a symbol of eternal life, and a sign they were attentive to the eternal order of things.

New fire represents rebirth and renewal, just as eternal fire represents a continuing order. Both concepts occur widely in the world, and the Iroquois were typical. When an epidemic occurred among the tribe, all fires were extinguished and the ashes cleaned from the hearth. The shaman then kindled new fire and called upon the fire god to spare the tribe. Each family rekindled its own hearth from the new fire. Many tribes had similar customs; the Zuni permitted only a man who had been struck by lightning to kindle new fire.

The Scots until recent times practiced a needfire ceremony whenever an epidemic broke out among livestock. All hearth fires were put out and a new fire kindled. *Needfire* comes from the Gaelic *teine-éiginn* meaning churned or forced fire, and had to be kindled by friction between pieces of wood, even after the invention of the match. The whole community took part. Sometimes an ox was sacrificed. When the needfire was burning the livestock were driven around it in groups of three, following the direction of the sun's path through the sky. The sun revives the world each spring, and needfire imitates the sun's role to warm the animals and deliver them from illness. American Indians often approached fire in the same way, for example by entering a tipi in a sunwise path around the central fire. It all suggests, somehow, ancient practices once more widespread in the world, and an old attentiveness to the need for sun and warmth.

The bonfire is another relic from the past. The word comes from *bonefire* and the time when bones were used for fuel; the old pronunciation may still be heard in Ireland. Today of course a bonfire does not require bones; it is any large fire around which people gather. The Bushmen of the Kalahari desert in Africa, among the last people to live by hunting and gathering wild food, still dance around such bonfires through the night. So do some American Indians. Anyone who has heard the sound of the Navajo night chant knows, even if he does not fully understand, the power that such ceremonies may have even for the spectator from an alien culture. This power is a reminder of links deep within us to people, and to ways, of the remote human past, when fires were marvelous and holy things.

In recent times the tendency has been to enclose fire in a furnace and lodge it in the cellar out of sight, where it runs automatically and may on occasion be attended by the oil- or gas-burner mechanic—rarely by the householder, who lacks knowledge of such things. Or the fire comes to us in the form of electricity sent along wires from a monster hearth at a utility, of which we know little or nothing, and over which we have no real control. Just possibly in this age of nuclear fires, it is time to regain some control over an element central to our lives, and to restore some of the attentiveness and respect for fire that even our remote ancestors knew.

Chapter 2

Open Hearths, Great Stoves, Small Dogs

In these halls the fireplace was anciently always in the middle of the room, till the Whigs removed it to one side.

Dr. Johnson at Oxford, 1754

The human race probably evolved in the warm environment of Africa and moved from there to colder regions—Europe, north Asia, North America. Just how we survived those colder regions in the beginning remains unclear. For a long time fire was thought to be the answer. But Catherine Perlès of the University of Paris has pointed out that some early sites of human habitation in Europe show no sign of fire at all.

Perhaps humanity is tougher than I feel I am on a cold winter night in New England. Perhaps it was not so terribly cold during the initial period of human residence in the north, and indeed there is evidence for that. Even today much of Europe remains far milder in winter than the northern reaches of the U.S. One can imagine wintering over wide areas of Europe at present without fire, provided shelter and warm clothing were at hand. Were these available? We have bone and ivory needles that were very likely used to sew clothing seventeen thousand years ago. Fur clothing may have appeared long, long before—sometime in the lower Palaeolithic, three million to one hundred thousand years ago.

Shelter is ancient. The simplest huts offer protection even without fire, and with fire can be quite comfortable. Fire in a 500-cubic-foot hut of skins maintains temperatures between 60° and 70°F inside while it is 25°F outside. About 150,000 years ago someone built and heated a hut of just this size in southern France. The builder laid poles against the wall of a small cave overlooking the sea, then covered the poles with animal hides, anchoring these to the earth with stones. There were two hearths, though one would have been characteristic for such a dwelling.

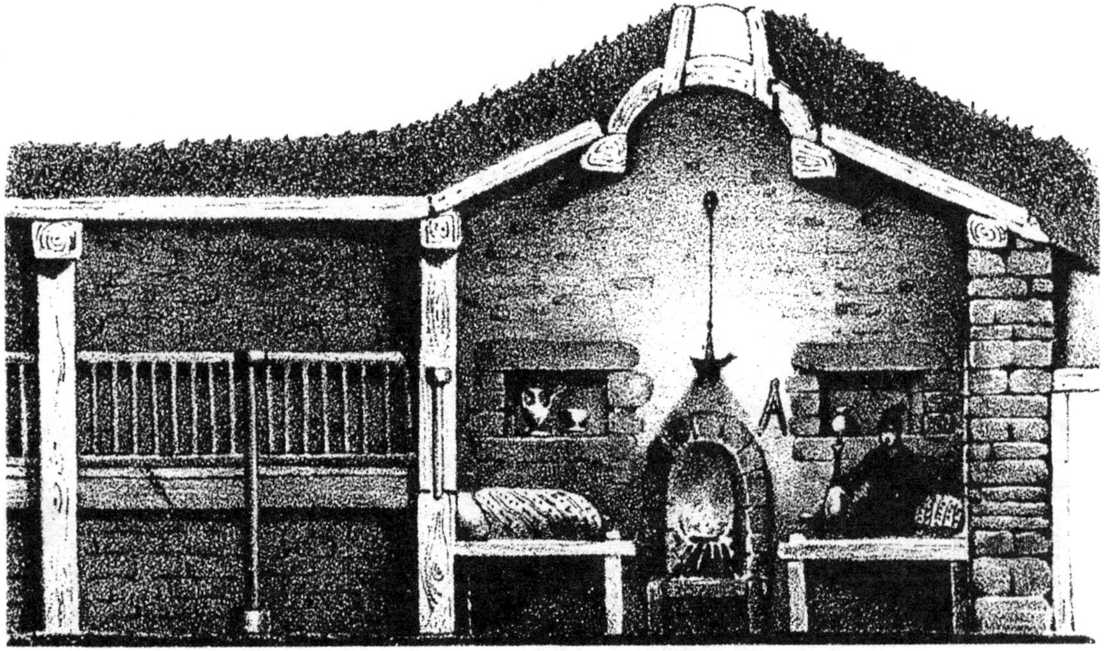

Figure 9 Smoke emerged through a vent in the roof of this semi-subterranean Armenian dwelling. Livestock may have occupied area at left. From *Voyage autour du Caucase* by Dubois de Montpéreux, Paris 1839. Reproduced by permission of The British Library.

In an Open Hearth House

In the [Serbian] villages, picturesquely located on the borders of the streams, or for greater security concealed in the fastnesses of the mountains, the low rude dwellings are at a distance from each other, and of such a size, that one not infrequently forms an entire street. Around the main room, which contains a hearth in the centre, are chambers for the young married people. Iron is scarcely used in the erection of Serbian dwellings, chimneys and windows are rare, the well-trodden earth serves for a floor, while the loam walls and bark roof are blackened with soot and smoke.

James O. Noyes, M.D.
Roumania, New York, 1857.

Early shelters were built of available materials. Hides spread over poles or the bones and tusks of mammoths formed a type widely used. Stone and clay were common early building materials. Usually there was only a single room, with the fire located at the center of the living area. In many parts of the world this pattern changed little from earliest times right up to the present. Smoke escaped from such dwellings as it could, through the low door or a smoke hole in the roof, or through the cracks, crannies, and crevices of buildings often carelessly made or in poor repair. The smoke wandered out through the roof, first blackening the interior of the hut with soot, and the rain trickled in. The Scots developed a special word, *snighe*, for rain that worked its way through the roof sods and dripped down black with soot upon the people below.

In these early shelters people slept on beds of furs, or rushes, straw, and leaves placed around an open fire. A bed of straw helped to block the damp rising from the ground. It could be cold, as contemporary studies show. Nighttime temperatures may be only 10°F or so above those outdoors inside open-hearth huts used today in the Andes or in Nepal. The pattern of life in such shelters seems to reflect very old ways. In the 1830s the British physician James Noyes, passing through Bulgaria, visited a peasant's hut "that serves him for cellar, granary, kitchen and bedroom. The family sleep on skins spread on the ground round the hearth which is a circular hole sunk in the middle of the room. Little more than the roof of these dark dwellings rises above the ground; you descend into them by a short flight of steps, and the doors are so low that you

must stoop as you enter. Nevertheless these poor huts are as clean and as neatly arranged inside as they can be made." The shelter sunk partly into the earth was apparently a common one from very early times in the Ukraine, Bulgaria, Rumania, Hungary, and regions to the north. Open-hearth houses remained in use in this part of the world, as well as in parts of western Europe and the British Isles, right up into the twentieth century.

STOVES-FOR-LIVING

Today the term *stove* refers to a certain kind of container for fire; the stove warms the room. In earlier times *stove* meant the heated room itself. The vast greenhouse at Kew Gardens in England used to be called the Great Stove, and early open-hearth dwellings were stoves in this old sense. They actually functioned as stoves. The dwelling was a container for the fire that burned on the open floor. A hole in the roof let the smoke out. The door admitted air for

Figure 10 Black house from the West of Scotland, lacking either a chimney or a hole in the roof to let the smoke out.

combustion, just as the adjustable air inlet does today on the door of an iron stove.

The so-called black houses of the Hebrides (islands off the west coast of Scotland) were examples of this kind of stove-for-living. They were named for their dark and sooty interiors, for they lacked even a smoke hole in the roof. Black houses were occupied into the twentieth century, but they appear to be of a very old type, related in style to the Bronze Age huts of Skara Brae in Orkney. The typical black house appears to be a pile of stone surmounted by a straw heap. As one observer put it, the house looks like a steaming dunghill in wet weather with smoke filtering out through the thatch wherever it can. The walls are five to nine feet thick. There are inner and outer walls of rough stone laid up without mortar, and the space between is filled in with turf.

In an iron stove, one speeds or slows combustion by adjusting the air supply to the fire. In the black house the door very crudely filled this role. But the black house typically had only one door and no smoke hole, which made for a particularly murky interior. The beehive houses of Scotland's Western Isles, and the central-hearth houses of Ireland, normally had two doors. Whichever door lay on the side away from the wind was used to adjust the draft; it was a more satisfactory arrangement. American Indians did much the same with their tipis, lifting the skins on one side as a draft adjustment for the fire that lay on the open

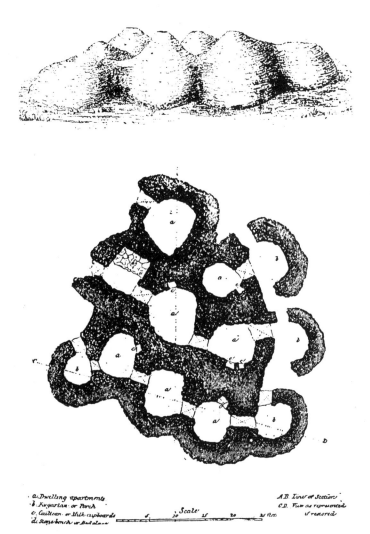

Figures 11 and 12 The stone beehive houses of western Scotland came in attached and detached forms. When clustered, the dwellings helped warm each other. Figure 12 shows the ground plan for the cluster shown in figure 11, with the view taken along the line C–D. Such structures remained in use on the Isle of Lewis in the nineteenth century.

floor. The open-hearth house normally lacked windows altogether. There might be a small hole or two in the wall, closable with a wooden shutter, or for draft adjustment. These were the "wind eyes" from which our windows descend. Light came in from the smoke hole in the roof (if any), from the door, and from the fire.

Within the central-hearth house the occupants sat in a ring about the fire, dogs and children sometimes lying in the warm ashes. Custom in the black house assigned the left side of the fire to women, the right to men. This appears to be a particularly old and widespread custom; the Sioux, the Mongols, the Irish, and doubtless others share it. The central fire, accessible from all directions, allowed the maximum number of people to draw near it. The floor was of packed earth or clay in the ordinary dwelling, and people sat on this or on low stools or benches. In some northern areas of the British Isles, a dialect word for bench, *dais*, referred to a log behind the fire. Benches were often for sleeping as well as sitting. In some Norwegian huts, the benches lining walls near the central hearth were closed in and filled with earth to block air infiltration through wall chinks.

The atmosphere within the chimney-less dwelling must have varied a great deal. The Indian tipi, with adjustable smoke flaps, can dispose of smoke quite well. So can the thatched farmhouse with its tall and steeply pitched roof. But in dwellings built low to the ground, like

the black house, there is less room overhead to accommodate the smoke pall. So it hangs there, perhaps three or four feet above the floor, trying to find its way out. It becomes important in such dwellings to keep the head low, as an old verse from the Western Isles of Scotland suggests:

By sitting low on rushes spread,
The smoke still hover'd overhead;
And did more good than real harm,
Because it kept the long house warm.

The smoke hole in the roof was normally offset so that rain would not fall directly on the fire. Sometimes, as in

Figure 13 Greek dwelling from before the chimney era. Smoke emerges from the hole at the peak of the roof.

Figure 15   Open hearth from an English hall like that in figure 14.

Figure 14   Sixteenth-century Gothic hall in England, with hearth in the middle of the floor, dining tables and benches along the sidewalls, and a gallery for musicians at rear.

Scandinavia, there was a louver in the roof, a kind of trapdoor that could be opened and closed with a pole. During the early and smoky stages of the fire the louver (the word comes from the French for opening, *l'ouvert*) was opened. It was closed to keep the heat in after the fire had burned down to charcoal and offered little smoke. In the manors and larger buildings of England, louvers became quite elaborate architectural features. Instead of simple trapdoors, they took the form of cupolas. These blocked the rain but let out the smoke in winter and the heat in summer.

The atmosphere in the central-hearth building depended on various factors, including the design of the building,

Figure 16   This smoke louver on the roof of Lincoln College, Oxford, was similar in form to the cupola of today. The smoke louver provided a means of letting the smoke out of large halls like that shown in figure 14, where open fires burned on central hearths.

weather, the quality of fuel and its moisture content, and the skill of the fire-tender. By present-day standards, conditions must have left a good deal to be desired. The English peasant immortalized in *Piers Plowman* had smarting eyes and a cough from the smoke in his medieval dwelling. He cursed those whose duty it was to provide dry wood and blow the fire into flame. Chaucer vividly described conditions in the widow's dwelling in *The Nun's Priest's Tale:* "Fful sooty was hir bour and eke her halle." Blackened roof beams that survive in buildings from the Middle Ages tell us the widow's sooty bower and hall were standard for the time. A king might assign a servant to full-time fire-tending, with results that were probably better than in the peasant's hut. But the king's fire was also in the middle of the floor, where drafts could blow smoke and ashes about. The king's eyes too must have smarted.

Still there were real advantages to the chimneyless house. The fire on the floor offers all its heat to the room; it is 100 percent efficient. The chimneyed fireplace offers a meager 10 percent efficiency as a rule, channeling 90 percent of the heat outdoors. The central hearth also saved woodcutting at a time when woodcutting tools were poor. Long sticks could be fed gradually into the fire. And there was room for more people close to the warmth. Many continued to use the open hearth, including some of the colleges of Oxford, long after the chimney became known. Habit was surely a factor; but so were the real advantages of the fire in the middle of the floor.

CHIMNEYS

Chimneys were known to Han China two thousand years ago, but it seems clear that the chimney principle was known long before that, perhaps before the advent of agriculture. The principle was almost surely understood in a practical sense by kiln and furnace builders in the Middle East, several thousand years before Christ. In Europe the Romans used a form of chimney two thousand years ago to carry off smoke from their hypocausts, which provided heat beneath the floor.

Despite all these early and successful examples, it took Europeans until very recent times to turn to the chimney en masse. It would be a mistake, I believe, to suppose that this was due to ignorance. During the four hundred years of their occupation of Britain, the Romans built many hypocausts. In the course of that time native Britons surely became familiar with the Roman system of smoke exhaust. Yet once the Romans departed, the Britons retired to their smoky huts; they let the Roman villas fall into ruins and their elaborate baths and heating systems with them. Virtually the same thing happened over most of Europe as Rome declined. Advanced Roman techniques fell into disuse. It is puzzling to the modern viewpoint, but there seemed a true resistance to the idea of the chimney.

As late as the sixteenth century, a conservative in England could still criticize the chimney as a decadent and even effeminate innovation. Smoke sent up the flue represented a loss of good medicine. This was not simply the opinion of one eccentric Englishman; it is an idea that was rather widely held in the world at one time. American Indians still use smoke as a ceremonial purifying element. The Irish used to carry a bit of soot (the residue from smoke) on a journey for luck. People of the sauna culture in northern Europe used open smoky fires to heat the bath and gave this up very reluctantly; some adopted the chimney only because fire insurance was otherwise prohibitive.

Certain tribesmen of Madagascar held a very high regard for smoke, according to Prof. Pierre Deffontaines, a student of human geography. These people developed a dense smoke pall in their huts by burning green wood and grass. They regarded smoke as almost sacred. A well-born person was said to be "black with soot," and a thick coating of soot in the house was a sign of the family's venerable history. The worst thing one person could say to another was, "You may no longer partake of our smoke."

Peculiar as they may seem to the modern mind, such attitudes may have reasonable origins. Smoke can be practical. On the seacoast of Chad in Africa, the daytime cooking fire burns outside. At night there is a fire in the shelter to drive off insects. The Lapps use a smoke hole in winter dwellings but none in summer, when they retain smoke to discourage insects. Anyone who has experienced the biting flies and mosquitoes of the far north or the tropics will understand why smoke may be preferable, and may seem endowed with magical qualities. In the preindustrial era in Europe of course, when most of the population survived by farming, there were eminently practical reasons for smoke in the dwelling. There was meat to be smoked; if it could be smoked above the household fire, that saved gathering wood for a separate fire. Crops were also dried as they lay on

Figure 18   In a Japanese house smoke from the open hearth typically emerged through a latticed opening at the gable end. Gable-end smoke outlets were sometimes used in Europe as well.

Figure 17   The hearth in this nineteenth-century Japanese dwelling was a board frame filled with sand.

platforms high up above the living area, amongst the rafters. The value of smoke in curing food seems likely to have weighed heavily against the chimney's use in many regions. This would have been especially true where damp weather made difficult the field drying of crops.

In the black houses of the Hebrides there was another reason to keep the smoke inside. Each year in spring the householders removed the thatch from the roof and spread it on the fields as fer-

tilizer. The lack of a smoke hole made for maximum soot buildup in the thatch and turned it into better fertilizer. The people of Achill Island in Ireland used to build special soot huts. These were five-by-ten-foot stone structures with sod roofs. Usually they were located out in the fields, and from October to May smoky fires fueled with damp turf burned inside them. In spring the blackened sods were removed from the roof and spread on the fields. E. Estyn Evans, the geographer and folklorist, thought the practice was at one time more general in Ireland, and that it might well recall the early beginnings of agriculture when crops were sown on the enriched soils of woodland freshly burned. Even today after burning the forest, the primitive slash-and-burn agriculturist spreads the ash before planting. In Ireland the forests had disappeared. But as Evans wrote in his book, *Irish Folk Ways*, "Faith in the use of fire persisted longer than the woods."

A Swedish View of England

Anyone acquainted with English houses during the colder part of the year can hardly avoid noticing, if he is Swedish, that the fireplaces have no dampers. One who is used to almost hermetically tight rooms can hardly understand how this is possible in the not-too-warm climate of England. The English, however, like damp air and drafts; they ignore the wind playing through the chimneys, half-opened windows and chinks. . . . In old English country houses, you often find very wide and heavy chimneys through which you . . . can look up to the stars in the sky. I have asked old people in both England and Scotland how it is possible to stand this . . .

Sigurd Erixon,
"Spjället, en Exponent För Svensk Bostadsteknik,"
Svenska Kulturbilder, Stockholm, 1937.

In North America some early settlers used the chimneyless central hearth for heat. But this was a temporary expedient, designed to save time and labor in construction. The fireplace-with-chimney swiftly became the dominant heating mode in the colonies as in England. Fireplace heat really is not adequate for the subzero winters of the northern U.S. and Canada. Better systems were available; colonists from central Europe built advanced tile stoves in Pennsylvania, North Carolina, and probably elsewhere. Brick stoves were built in New England and Nebraska. But the dominant group of colonists came from the British Isles. To them heat meant fireplaces, and their style set the standard. Fireplaces remained the dominant heating method until the manufactured iron stove came along, primarily in the nineteenth century.

Figure 19 This English fireplace had space for a bench, common practice in an era when the interior of the house at any distance from the hearth might be quite cold.

Early fireplaces tended to be large. They might contain a seat or bench next to the fire. The great size (some American fireplaces were six to nine feet across) reduced woodcutting and allowed more people close to the flames. Size was important also to provide work space. Great iron pots simmered over the fire on farms to provide food for man and beast alike. Henry Fabre, the French naturalist, described the "enormous redoubt" covering one whole side of a room that held the fireplace of his nineteenth-century French schoolroom. The hearth itself lay in the middle, but on the left and right, sheltered beneath the mantel, lay two beds recessed at breast height into the stonework. Two favored boarders in the schoolmaster's house slept in these. With perhaps a touch of envy, Fabre wrote in *The Life of the Fly*, "They must lie snug in there at night, with their shutters closed, when the north wind howls at the mouth of the dark valley and sends the snow awhirl." A salt box hung against the fireplace wall; the warmth kept it dry. A long pine branch leaned against the stonework. Its center had been burned out with a hot iron, and it was used to blow coals into life. The privileged boarders sat on stools in the best location before the fire, over which great caldrons of pig food cooked. "We others sitting on our heels formed a semi-circle around those big caldrons, full to the brim and giving off little jets of steam, with puff-puff-puffing sounds."

Figure 20 German domestic scene, circa 1618. Note long sticks of wood standing beyond hearth, bellows used to blow sparks into flame, spark hood over fire. The raised hearth represented progress; the housewife need not crouch to deal with the fire.

Figure 21 In some areas of Europe, the methods of 1618 hung on into the present century. This kitchen scene is from the Austrian Tyrol in 1936. Photo by Erika Groth-Schmachtenberger.

Shelter magazines illustrate the scene often, in a spirit of nostalgia: The open fire, the colonial family gathered around, the pot hung from a crane over the coals. Undeniably it's an attractive scene. But by the tens of thousands Americans bricked up their handsome fireplaces as iron stoves became readily available. The fireplace used vast amounts of wood. It gave too little heat. It must also have been a trial for the woman who had to use it for cooking. With the affluence of the oil age we have uncovered the old fireplaces in colonial homes. But today they are objects of aesthetic delight, not work spaces or devices for serious heating. And some of them, once again, are being bricked up in favor of stoves.

Figure 22 Benches with reversible backs date from fourteenth-century France. One could face the fire, or turn the backrest about and warm the back.

America Two Hundred Years Ago

A hundred years ago not a pound of coal nor a cubic foot of illuminating gas had been burned. No iron stoves, no friction matches had been used, and all the cooking and warming in town or country were done by the aid of a fire kindled on the brick hearth or in the brick ovens. Pine knots and tallow candles furnished the light for the long winter nights and sanded floors supplied the place of rugs and carpets. Only one room in the house was warm, unless some member of the family was ill, in all the rest the temperature was at zero during many nights of the winter. Think of all this in the Christmas time and be as kind to others as providence has been good to you.

From the Jefferson City (Mo.) *State Journal*, January, 1877.

ANIMAL WARMTH

Fire was not the only source of warmth in the prestove era. The human body generates heat. In a cooler environment it loses that heat into its surroundings. A person in a cool room, then, tends to warm the room. The effect may not be significant; the room may dissipate the heat as quickly as it is received. But with several people gathered the effect is greater and the room may warm noticeably. The human race has long used this knowledge in cold weather, gathering in closer communal arrangements for warmth and then dispersing in smaller groups in warm weather. Traditional living patterns among the Eskimos, the Mongols, and others offer examples.

The old farms of rural Norway had many buildings. These might include a bathhouse, blacksmith shop, storehouses, cookhouse, stable, byre or cowhouse, *aarestue* or hearth room, and others. Separation limited fire loss. If the cook house burned, the food supply survived in the storehouse. The hearth room was where the family, and often all the servants as well, slept in winter. In summer they dispersed, moving for privacy into other buildings during the time when heat was less necessary. A similar pattern occurred on Russian farmsteads, and I'm sure elsewhere. It was a pattern that conserved fuel and allowed all to share warmth created by the group.

In the same way people have long used warmth generated by their domestic animals. Sometimes the livestock occupied the ground floor of the building and the people the floor above, where the animals' warmth would reach them. An alternative pattern placed the family at one end of a longhouse and the livestock at the other. As an old verse from Britain puts it, "At one of th' ends he kept his cows,/At th' other end he kept his spouse."

Farmhands often slept in the byre end of the house with the cows, warmed both by the animals and the fermenting manure. In the Celtic fringes of Britain there was a belief that milk yield increased if cows were kept indoors in winter. It was important too that the cows see the fire, which drove off evil spirits. In Ireland some of these old beliefs hung on until recent times, in the taking of newborn cows through the house for luck, or in driving mature cows into the house for milking.

Cutting and moving enough wood for winter warmth may require a major effort. The fact was not lost on some of our ancestors as they considered ways around this chore. In the valley of the Maurienne in France, Pierre Deffontaines noted that until the nineteenth century people quartered sheep beneath their beds at night for warmth. These would have been high beds, raised well above cool drafts close to the floor. And very likely they were beds closed in by curtains or shutters, as many were in past eras both for privacy and for warmth.

Also in the Maurienne Valley stables were sometimes dug into the earth, and people gathered in them in winter to sleep, enjoying the warmth generated by livestock, manure, and other people. School sessions were held in stables in some French communities, according to Deffontaines, and in one area of what is now Yugoslavia women used to gather in winter to do embroidery in rooms hollowed out of great heaps of manure, which as it fermented kept them warm.

Shepherds and herdsmen have long used their animals for warmth when caught out in cold weather. When caught in a blizzard, Siberian reindeer herders would force two deer to the ground and lie between them. The expression "three-dog night" testifies to the warming value of dogs. In the cathedrals of England one can still see the sculpted likeness of many a deceased nobleman of yore. He rests on his back on the lid of his sarcophagus, with his feet against the back of a small crouching dog. The ascent to heaven was perhaps not more likely, but it was surely more comfortable with warm feet.

Servants in England were sometimes required to hold the master's feet against their bodies for warmth. Lap dogs were beloved pets; they were also utilitarian foot and stomach warmers. In colonial America, citizens sometimes brought their dogs to church to serve as footrests. But given enough dogs this practice led to a certain disruptive clamor; the ministry discouraged it.

Over thousands of years man has developed a great many breeds of dog. The function is usually clear: hunting, guarding, retrieving, herding. But the hairless breeds always puzzled me, until I learned they were used as heaters. The Mexican hairless seems to derive from an older hairless breed that originated in China. Deffontaines mentions a third, found in the mountains of Bolivia and used specifically for its value as a heater. Lacking insulation, the hairless is perhaps a better conductor. But far more important, the hairless is easily kept free of fleas, a vital consideration in intimate companions.

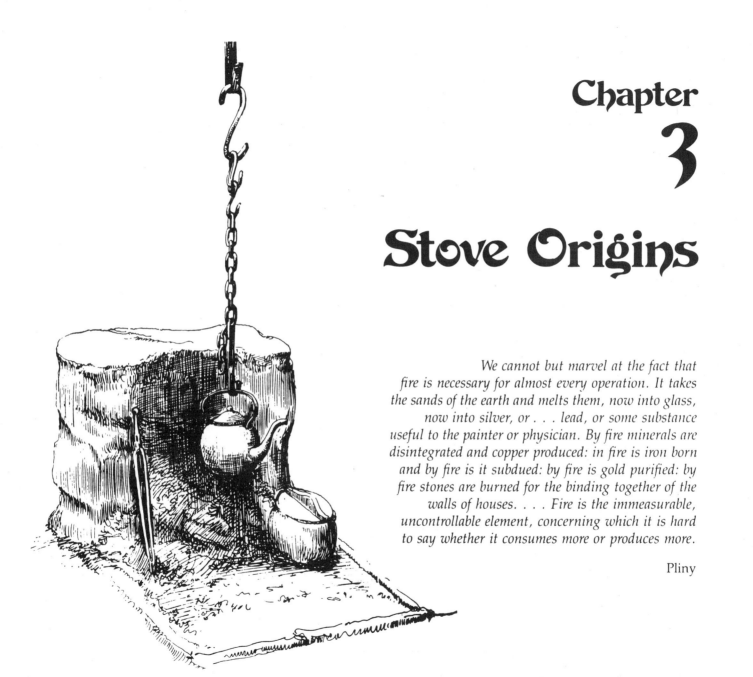

Chapter
3

Stove Origins

We cannot but marvel at the fact that fire is necessary for almost every operation. It takes the sands of the earth and melts them, now into glass, now into silver, or . . . lead, or some substance useful to the painter or physician. By fire minerals are disintegrated and copper produced: in fire is iron born and by fire is it subdued: by fire is gold purified: by fire stones are burned for the binding together of the walls of houses. . . . Fire is the immeasurable, uncontrollable element, concerning which it is hard to say whether it consumes more or produces more.

Pliny

If you look at the human use of fire over the past one and a half million years, three periods of change stand out.

Period one began about one hundred thousand years ago. Before that time, the use of fire was exceptional; after that time, it was the rule. We don't know just why. One theory is that in the long earlier time span humans did not know how to make fire and had to steal it from the fire spirits, so to speak—from forest fires and volcanoes, as in the myths. Then about one hundred thousand years ago humans learned to make fire through friction between two pieces of wood, or by striking sparks. Thereafter, the use of fire became common. The theory is reasonable. It may well be true.

Period two began about ten thousand years ago with the advent of agriculture in the Middle East. The societies of the eastern Mediterranean developed rapidly at that time the fire-using crafts that form the base for our own industrial age: metal smelting and the making of pottery, plasters, cements, and glass. There was also bread baking, to make palatable the grains produced by a budding agriculture. After one and a half million years of slow change in the uses of fire, these developments just before the birth of Christ came like an explosion, a sudden flowering in the uses and techniques of pyrotechnology. They helped set in motion the forces that still govern, support, and bedevil our own age.

Period three covers our own industrial revolution, the past few hundred years.

It is the time when the small-scale crafts of period two became the vast fire-using industries of period three. It has been a time of fuel crises, new energy sources, searches for more efficient combustion, and concern about those products of combustion known as air pollution. More about period three in the next chapter. In the meantime consider the first two periods, which provided prototypes for today's stoves and furnaces.

Virtually every principle known to today's wood-stove user seems to have its origin in the prehistoric past. The idea of the grate, of draft, and the chimney principle, of airtightness, of the closed stove as opposed to the open fire, and even of forced draft—all these go back, I believe, to a time before the age of metals and possibly even of agriculture. To use the expression of Theodore A. Wertime, anthropologist at the Smithsonian Institution, they were ideas waiting in the wings for their time to come. That time came with the development of agriculture. It came with the birth of cities and of civilization with all its pyrotechnological demands.

Hearths of the remote past—the earliest structured means of controlling and dealing with fire—came in a variety of types: shallow depressions in the earth; hearths walled around by an earth berm or dry-stone wall; raised hearths built on blocks of stone; and the so-called vented hearths, pits dug into the earth with channels leading up to them, which carried air to the base of the fire. All of

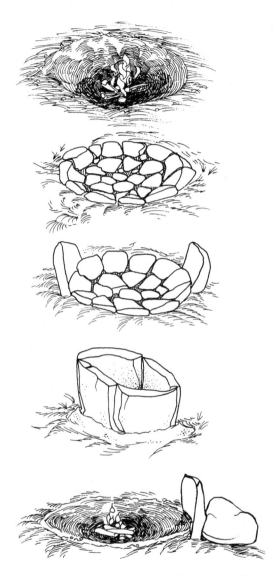

Figure 23 Prehistoric hearth types. From top: a simple depression in the earth; depression lined with stone; depression lined and ringed with stone; ovenlike pit lined with stone; stone-at-the-head-of-the-fire. After C. Perlès.

these hearth types appeared one hundred thousand to thirty-five thousand years ago. More recently, between thirty-five thousand and twelve thousand years ago, two more types appeared: hearths covered over with stones, and ovenlike enclosures.

Three prehistoric hearths have special interest as possible auguries of things to come: the vented pit hearth, the ovenlike enclosure, and the pile of heated rocks.

PROTOFURNACE

Existence of the vented pit hearth in preagricultural times rests on thin evidence. There are very few examples, and from the scientist's viewpoint there are basic questions about even these. Was the channel to the pit in fact dug out intentionally? If so, was it done to channel air to the fire? There may never be unequivocal answers.

Still I believe there is sound reason to think that the vented pit hearth is a very old device, known well before the flowering of agriculture. Possibly its use came about in this way: Where water tables are high or rain frequent, pits get water in them. Drainage becomes essential before fire-building, and there is at least one observation of an American Indian digging a channel to his fire pit for this reason. Both the need and the solution seem obvious, and very likely ancient. Once such a channel is present, it's also obvious that the fire burns bet-

ter. There remains only the question of putting this knowledge to use.

I believe the knowledge *was* put to use during period one, and that the evidence for this may in time come to light. We do know that use of this particular bit of knowledge burgeoned during period two as early kilns and furnaces appeared. With the passage of time, heating devices became more and more specialized by function during period two—for metal smelting, for glassmaking, for firing pottery, and so on. But in the beginning there appears to have been a more generalized form of furnace closely resembling the vented hearth, and which had many uses. This was a pit or shaft dug vertically into the earth, often in a hillside. Air reached the fire in the base of the pit through a tunnel. In a hillside this tunnel would cut horizontally inward to the base of the pit. On level ground the air tunnel would commence off to one side of the pit and angle downward to the base. Pit furnaces of this type have been used for metal smelting, lime kilning, firing pottery, cooking, baking, and doubtless other functions. In some parts of the world these uses continue today. Thus the vented pit furnace seems a good candidate for the sort of generalized device, dating back before the advent of agriculture, from which later and more specialized types may derive.

The design of this protofurnace suggests two things about the people who used it. One, they understood the value

Figure 24 One of the simplest and most ancient forms of furnace remains in use today. This protofurnace is used to refine sugar in Laos. Note how the arrangement permits use of uncut logs as fuel, saving labor. FAO photo by H. A. Wirtz.

Figure 25 African iron-smelting furnace in use in the nineteenth century, built in the protofurnace mode but above ground rather than dug into the earth.

Figure 26 Japanese kitchen range, nineteenth century. This simple cooking range in the protofurnace mode was of a type widely used around the world.

Figure 27 A lime-burning kiln from Denmark, again in the protofurnace style.

Figure 28 Forge of Hephaistus shown on a Greek vase of the sixth century B.C.

Figure 29 Furnace for roasting and quenching gold ore in sixteenth-century Europe. Note tied bundles of faggots at right, a common fuel. The height of the structures in figures 25, 28, and 29 suggests an understanding of chimney principles, dating back in the case of figure 28 more than two thousand years before chimneys became common in Europe.

of *channeling* air to the base of the fire; they had a practical understanding not only of what makes combustion work but of what will improve its working. This is emphasized by the fact that in the Middle East the air tunnel of early furnaces seems to have been oriented purposely to take advantage of prevailing winds. (The bellows soon supplanted the wind in this function.) Second, the vertical shaft portion of the furnace, especially as it grew in length, strongly suggests an understanding of draft and the chimney effect—and this thousands of years before chimneys were, so far as we know, ever used in dwellings. Another case, perhaps, of knowledge waiting in the wings.

OVENS

In 1951 at Dolni Vestonice in Czechoslovakia, excavators found the twenty-five thousand year old site of a mammoth hunter's hut. Within the hut was a central hearth. Surrounding the hearth were the remains of a vaulted kiln or ovenlike structure, a dome of some kind that had been made of clay mixed with limestone grit. The clay had a reddish color, indicating that it had been fired. Scattered about the floor of the hut were more than two thousand fragments of fired clay, including the heads of two bears and a fox.

The clay figures were presumably fired in the oven, which defines it as a kiln, and as such the oldest known ancestor of the potter's kiln. The device may also have been used for preparing food or for other purposes—we do not and may never know. Whatever the function, kiln or oven or both, it is the most ancient device of its kind ever found. From the description, the structure evidently resembled in shape the simple clay baking ovens of later ages.

In France at roughly the same period, someone built two stone-lined pits that have also been described as ovens, though in fact their use does not seem clear. Four or five stone slabs formed the sides of the pit, leaning inward a bit so that the opening at the top was somewhat smaller than the base. The opening at the top was ten to fifteen inches on a side, and the depth about eight inches. Most remarkably, perhaps, the joints between the stone slabs were filled in with small stones embedded in a mortar made of clay, sand, and limestone. So far as I know this represents the earliest use of mortar, and of limestone in that role. Similar mortars played an important part in the emergence of civilization thousands of years later, and also in early stoves and ovens.

There is a second interesting aspect to these French fire pits with their stone slab sides. Many thousands of years later at Timna in Palestine, when the age of metals had arrived, an almost identical pit was used as a crucible for melting copper. This is not to suggest that the French fire pits were used to process

Figure 30 Roman domed oven from the first century B.C. At right, men kneading dough. This frieze was a part of the monument to the baker Eurysaces. Courtesy Oxford University Press.

Figure 31 Clay baking oven from Hungary. Note blackened roof beams above.

metal; there is no evidence whatever that they were. But it does suggest the existence, long before the age of metals, of some of the technology needed to form and deal with them; once again, knowledge waiting in the wings.

The familiar domed shape of the clay oven emerged very early. The oldest I have heard of, aside from that at Dolni Vestonice, is from a site excavated by Marija Gimbutas in Thessaly, northern Greece. There in a Neolithic village inhabited more than eight thousand years ago, several ovens were uncovered that look virtually identical to many clay ovens built today. "They were used very probably for baking bread," Prof. Gimbutas reported, "and also for ritual purposes, because there are platforms next to the ovens on which were placed figurines of a pregnant goddess."

More about ovens in later chapters.

ROCK STOVES

Rocks appear in very early hearths, and there are many possible reasons for placing them there. For example:

- A ring or wall of rocks built around the hearth will contain a fire.

- Rocks placed under fuel permit air to circulate, promoting better combustion. We use grates and andirons for the same purpose today.

- Hot stones have long been used for cooking food and for drying food to preserve it.

- The sauna or sweat bath traditionally uses stones as a source of warmth.

- Various Stone Age industries required the heating of rock, as in the making of ochre, for use in tanning or painting.

Stone for tools was heated to improve workability at least twenty thousand years ago. Early man also quarried stone with fire, heating rock and then splitting it by sudden cooling with water.

Precisely when people began placing stones in fire to store heat may never be entirely clear. A cat knows enough to sit after sunset on a rock still warm from the sun. Early humans are unlikely to have missed the same connection, working constantly as they did with fire and stone. Some methods and ideas that have survived until recent times may, in this respect, reflect very old ways. Consider, for example, a type of hearth found in Europe right up to the twentieth century. This was a raised rectangular hearth, rising perhaps a foot above the floor. The sides were stone slabs, or wood lined with clay; the interior was filled with stones, which of course retained heat. At the head of the hearth stood a vertical stone slab, set in place like a gravestone; against this the fire was built.

The stone slab had several functions: It kept sparks from flying out in one direction. It reflected heat, as well as helped to contain the fire. It served as a backstop against which the coals could be banked and covered with ashes to preserve the fire overnight. People in rural Norway installed such hearths until late in the nineteenth century. They differed little from hearths built two thousand years before in the Bronze Age huts of Skara Brae, on the island of Orkney. In photos taken by Prof. Leroi-Gourhan in France of hearths used by Magdalenian hunters fifteen thousand to eighteen thousand years ago, you can see the same pattern, though the hearth is not raised: a cluster of smaller stones with a much larger stone block set at the edge of it.

Now none of this would be especially remarkable, except for the fact that in Wales there is a legend about such hearths and about the big stone set at the edge. In Wales this stone was called the *pentanfaen*, or stone-at-the-head-of-the-fire. Once this stone had been set in place, it was a violation of old Welsh law to remove it. The people might move from the house; the house might fall or burn. The *pentanfaen* must be left standing nevertheless, as the sign of an occupied homestead to which the owners might return if they wished. Until quite recent times in Norway, such hearths served also as altars, and sacrifices were made there to the household gods.

At some uncertain point in history, there came a change in the way people piled rocks on the hearth. The pile acquired structure. The rocks were stacked to create a chamber and the fire burned inside it. We know that early Slavic groups used such rock ovens fourteen hundred years ago, in the semiunderground dwellings that they built then in the Ukraine. To the north, the Baltic peoples, Scandinavians, and Finns have used them right up into the twentieth century.

The rock stove represents an advance over the open hearth because of its heat storage capacity. But another factor may well have weighed more heavily with the people who used them: spark protection. Sparks rising from an open fire represent a threat, especially so in the log dwelling commonly built by forest dwellers of north and east Europe. Over a good bit of this region, the common fuel is softwood, which produces an especially heavy spark output—much heavier than that of hardwoods common over more southerly areas of Europe. Rock and clay stoves may, then, have had a protective role at least as important as their heating function.

Figure 32 Pit hearths, used for cooking and other purposes, were often lined with clay or stone. This prehistoric hearth is drawn from an undated model.

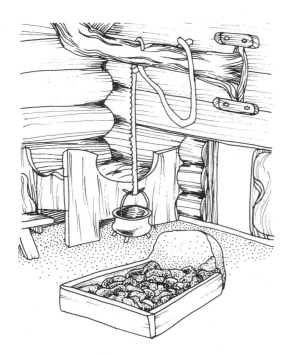

Figure 33 Stone-pile hearth in a Norwegian farmhouse. Stone standing at the head of the fire served various purposes, including blocking the draft from the doorway beyond.

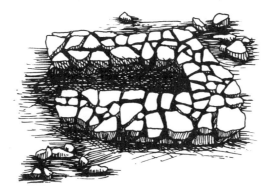

Figures 34 and 35 Two stone-pile stoves from a thirteenth-century Latvian hill fort, drawn from a photograph.

Rock stoves, of course, poured their smoke into the dwelling, just as the open fire had done. In Norway they were called smoke stoves, *røkovnen*. Sometimes they were built of stones of moderate size, sometimes of real boulders and even of heavy quarried slabs. The pattern varied. But the larger ones, as suggested by the accompanying illustrations, stored large amounts of heat.

Figure 36 Combination cooking hearth and oven, all built from great slabs of stone in an Austrian peasant dwelling.

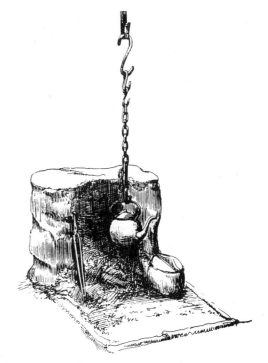

Figure 37 Stone-at-the-head-of-the-fire, or reredos. Shetland Islands.

SAUNA

When a farmer established his homestead in rural Finland in the old days, he built the sauna first and heated it with a rock stove. Other buildings might come later, but the sauna was essential; it was the heart of the farm's life. Women went there to give birth, the old to die. The sauna was the site of ceremonies when the young came of age, were betrothed or married. The sauna was the place where grain was dried, meat smoked, and malt dried to make beer. The sauna was the home of the sweat bath; it was the place that was warm in winter.

Figure 38 Sauna stove from Denmark. Similar stoves were used in drying kilns and to heat dwellings in Scandinavia and the east Baltic area.

The term *sauna* is Finnish. It refers to a particular kind of sweat bath. But closely related baths are widespread in the world and it is convenient to use the Finnish term for all of them. Igor Vahros defined a sauna culture across the northern forest zone of Europe and Asia, from Norwegian Lapland to Siberia and the Pacific. A form of sweat bath existed among the Eskimo and the North American Indians. The Irish used sweat baths and so did the ancient Scythians, as Herodotus recounts. Philologists, according to Tamara Habicht, trace the baths back four thousand years, through sauna terminology used by Finno-Ugrian peoples along the Baltic coast. But sauna history, and that of the rock stoves used in the sauna for heat, may go back much farther.

Sauna practice varies, but certain elements are common among many peoples. The idea is to build heat for a sweat bath within a shelter, and rocks heated in fire provide the warmth. In the course of the bath people often switch themselves (or each other) with a whisk to stimulate the skin, then rub down with scented herbs. The Finns, Russians, and American Indians traditionally use twig switches, often of birch. In the past Indians also used buffalo tails or eagle wings; the Estonians used wolf or fox tails. At some point the bather pours water over the rocks to produce vapor. The Finns tend to like a dry sauna and use little water; the Russians tend to like it moist and use a lot. Finally there is a plunge into cold water or snow. Sauna everywhere

used to be surrounded by myth and ritual; it was (and remains for many) a means of cleansing both body and spirit.

Black Elk, wise man of the Oglala Sioux, said that in the old days his people used their sweat lodges every day in winter, sometimes several times a day. "And from this we received our power." Today's lodge is often a round dome made of hides stretched over willow poles, holding perhaps half a dozen people. Older lodges are said to have been much larger, holding twenty and with larger rock piles for heat. Everything has its meaning: The lodge represents the universe and the rock pit in the floor its center. The red hot rocks represent the earth and the fire the light of the sun. In the Sioux language the word for fire carries with it the idea of eternity, the fire-of-no-end.

Figure 39 A painting by C. P. Elfstrom shows a Finnish sauna in 1808. Note rocks in stove at left.

Figure 40 Woman at left pours a dipper of water on the rock stove in this Finnish sauna. 1800.

For many in north Europe and Asia, the sauna was also once a place of ceremony, a holy place, as it has been for North American Indians. This spirit often remains in modern usage, though details and ceremonies have dropped away. Elves and spirits once inhabited the sauna; it was always a place where magic powers could be felt and spells cast. There were, however, also practical considerations. These relate to less sanitary conditions of the past. Igor Vahros recorded a child's verse from Russia:

The louse heats the sauna
The nit boils the soapy water
The cockroach splits the firewood.

In the Russian sauna pails and tubs of water stood at hand for washing, and bathers hung their clothing where heat might discourage tiny forms of wildlife that might inhabit it.

The sauna cleansed, it restored spirit and health. Among the Sioux and other Indians it also recalled the relationship between man and the surrounding universe. But not least of the bath's functions was warming, especially in the cold winter months when the sun was low, a pale reflection of its summer self, recalled for a brief time by the sauna's heat.

Today the sauna seems to be reaching new heights of popularity far beyond Finland and the east Baltic. Stoves may now be electric or gas-fired, but rocks retain their place in the stove. And though it boggles the mind of a New Englander, Finnish rocks are actually imported for this purpose to the U.S.

WALK-IN CHIMNEYS

Early in its evolution, the chimney began to assume gargantuan proportions in some European regions. The base area really became a small room. You could walk inside the chimney and a lot went on there: cooking, baking, the smoking and drying of food.

The walk-in chimney of east Denmark, for example, had a low, open doorway on one side. Along one side of the chimney room lay a raised bench built of stone or brick, and upon this the cooking fire burned. Nearby there were various small openings in the chimney wall. One led into the oven, which was fired from inside the chimney. A second opening might lead to the fire chamber beneath a caldron situated in an adjoining room. A third opening often led into a stove in another adjoining room. As with the oven, the stove was fed from inside the chimney, sometimes by shoveling coals or burning embers into it from the cooking fire.

Figure 41 Interior of a Danish walk-in chimney. At left rear, oven opening. At center, raised shelf held a cooking fire. At right, stokehole for a jamb stove or *billeger*. Lower right, stokehole for a protofurnace probably used to heat a caldron.

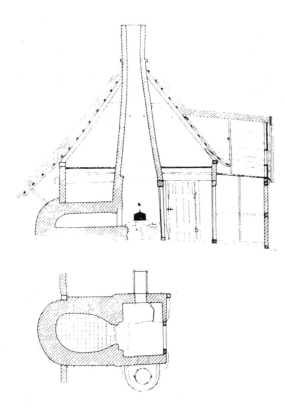

Figure 42 Plan of Danish cottage with walk-in chimney. Stokeholes opening off chimney were used to fire oven, jamb stove, and caldron.

A particularly massive type of walk-in chimney appeared in Poland and the east Baltic region. The room within the chimney base could be up to fourteen feet square with walls eighteen inches thick at the base and tapering as they rose toward the roof. Pauls Kundzins described the evolution of such chimneys in his book on the Latvian farmstead, *Latvju Sēta*. Because of the spark danger in wooden dwellings, people began coating wooden walls near the fire with a layer of clay. Then they began building domed spark-catchers over the fire itself. The dome was a woven framework of branches coated with clay. In time the spark catcher and clay-coated wooden walls were all replaced with solid masonry, including a vaulted masonry ceiling over the fire. The vault had a hold in the top so smoke could rise into the attic and out through the gable ends. The final step was an enclosed chimney to carry smoke directly out through the attic and the roof. A similar pattern of evolution—from open fire, to spark catcher, to vault, to chimney—emerged over much of Europe.

Latvians cooked over open fires within the chimney as did people in east Denmark. Coals and embers could be shoveled into stone or boulder ovens opening off the chimney. It was a crude and inefficient method of heating. But it was far safer than the open fire in a wooden dwelling, especially where the fire was of softwood. It also had the great virtue of offering, through the oven, heat without smoke in adjoining rooms. Meats were hung in the upper part of the chimney for curing; racks lower down served for drying crops. Tons and tons of clay and stone went into some of those chimneys. Once warmed they had a stabilizing effect on the temperature within the dwelling.

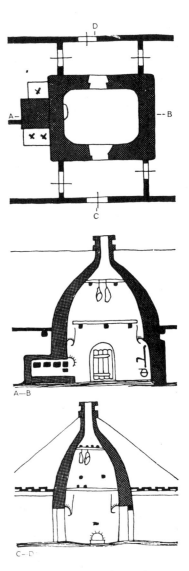

Figure 43 Massive walk-in chimneys were built in Latvia. Cooking and baking occurred on the lower level. Food dried on racks just above. Meat smoked on upper level. Chimney walls could be eighteen inches thick at the base and the chimney itself ten or more feet across.

DRYING KILNS

In the days before refrigeration, smoking and drying were important means of preserving food. But drying can be difficult in the cool rainy climate of northern Europe. Kilns offered a solution, especially where the fire risks—as in drying barley—might be very great if this were undertaken in the dwelling. In the east Baltic area and in Scandinavia, both drying kilns and sauna stoves were widely used. In time they emerged as multipurpose devices. In their development it seems likely that they contributed, along with the baking oven, to the evolution of the heat-storage stove.

A common form of drying kiln found in the east Baltic and in Scandinavia was the simple boulder stove, like that used in the sauna. It was a pile of rocks with a cave beneath for the fire. On a farm of any size, the kiln was set apart to diminish fire danger. Whatever was to be dried—grain, hops, malt for beer, flax—was laid out on a platform above the kiln. There was no chimney. The idea was to retain all heat and smoke inside the building. At most there was a hole to let the smoke out.

The preoccupation with accidental fire must have been constant around such kilns. The buildings were wooden. Barley heads were laid on flammable straw to dry. Softwood threw sparks. If the building burned, a por-

Figure 44 Danish drying kiln. Because of the risk from fire while drying barley heads in a kiln such as this, the kiln normally occupied a separate building.

tion of the food supply was likely to burn with it, and that might not easily be replaced. This was a terrible risk in a world without supermarkets. The pressure for design improvements must have been high around kiln buildings. And these improvements came. First the rock-pile stove was surrounded by a low masonry wall. Then it was covered over with a masonry vault. Both changes tended to keep the sparks in. The rocks were retained inside the kiln; they added to the heat storage capacity.

In Estonia and northern Latvia such

heating devices developed a fourfold purpose. In the region life centered around something known as the living/threshing barn. It was a log building with a thatched roof and one big heated room. The family used the room to thresh grain in the fall, then dried the grain there by the heat of the big kiln. In winter the family lived in the threshing room, using the kiln for warmth and cooking over an open fire built at the front of it. In some areas the same stove served also as the sauna, and the bathers threw water on the rocks inside the stove to create vapor.

In summer of course the heat-storage capacity of these kiln/stoves made them undesirable for cooking. In Finland, Estonia, and Latvia this led to a summer kitchen, which was a sort of pole tipi with an open central hearth.

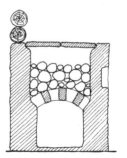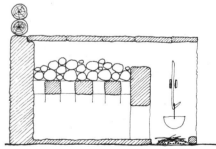

Figure 45 Clay and stone stove used for cooking, sauna, and as a drying kiln and heater in Estonia. Cooking took place over an open fire (right) at the front of the stove. There was no chimney. Courtesy of the Estonian State Open Air Museum.

In some areas its use survived well into the twentieth century. Students of east Baltic history believe it may have been the standard dwelling of very early inhabitants of the east Baltic region.

FIRE PRESERVATION

The modern iron or steel stove has two outstanding characteristics: a means of regulating the fire by controlling its air supply, and thin walls that conduct heat rapidly. Advertising often claims air control as a modern idea and the chief virtue of the airtight stove. U.S. patents on airtights date back about one hundred forty years. But the idea behind them was known widely to prehistoric people. Early man attempted to preserve fire, to keep it from dying. He often accomplished this just as the airtight stove does today, by limiting the air available to support combustion.

Walter Hough compiled a record of early fire preservation methods when he was curator of anthropology at the Smithsonian. The Cherokee Indians, he found, used to set a tinder-dry log on fire and then bury it in the ground, where it would smolder for days. The Osage Indians took a certain fungus from inside a hollow tree, set it afire and encased it in earth. Then they packed the earth into a mussel shell and wrapped and bound it tightly. With minute amounts of air available, the fire inside

held for days. In New Guinea the Matabut islanders would pack a hot coal in coconut fiber and put the whole thing in a coconut shell; the fire would remain alive three to four days. Fishermen in the region of Cape Finisterre in northwest Spain held smoldering material in a cow horn with its end plugged. When they needed fire they would pull the plug and blow the embers into flame. The Scots "smoored" the embers with ash to keep them alive until morning; so did our colonial ancestors in the U.S. The term curfew derives from the French *couvre-feu*, or cover-fire. The original curfew was a cover (often brass) placed over a heap of coals in the fireplace; it limited the air supply and kept the coals burning. The curfew bell signaled the time to cover the fire for the night.

Figure 46 Brass curfew, for covering coals to hold the fire overnight.

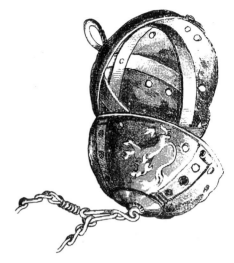

Figure 47 French chauferettes, for warming hands. These vessels came in a variety of sizes. Some held hot water, others charcoal or a piece of heated iron.

Hand- or pocket-warming devices were once widely used—a warm stone or brick, even a warm potato. Some derive from fire preservation methods. The Japanese sometimes still use a kind of belly-stove carried in a wrap-around sash about the waist. Once these were made of copper or tin with a perforated lid, and they were curved to fit the wearer. The fuel was powdered charcoal formed into a paper cartridge. When lighted it would produce a mild heat for several hours. Today Japanese belly-stoves are made of aluminum and lined with glass.

The legend of Prometheus carrying fire in a hollow fennel stalk suggests how old such fire preservation methods must be. The stalk seems clearly to have been a means of limiting air, as well as a container for the coals. The concept behind the airtight stove may have been forgotten from time to time, by one society or another. But it is truly ancient.

BRAZIERS

The brazier is a bowl-shaped device without a chimney, designed for burning charcoal or coal. Compared to the fireplace, it has the very great advantage of being portable. Some of the old ones had wheels and you could tow them about the house.

Braziers are for the most part heating devices of the milder climates. In antiquity they were used extensively around the Mediterranean, where in some areas

Figure 48   Wheeled brazier from England.

they remain in use. The usual practice is to light the brazier outdoors in early evening. When the charcoal is glowing and all the smoke is gone, the brazier is carried indoors.

North China has long had a form of central heating, but the south China climate is milder, and central heating is not required. Rudolf Hommel, traveling in south China in the 1930s, saw braziers in use everywhere, in the houses and in the fields. People carried bowls of glowing embers about on visits to neighbors. Seated, they held the brazier in their laps with their hands over it, or they set it on the floor and rested their feet on it. Braziers heated flat irons; they warmed baby chicks at night. A woman spinning might sit on a portable stool with a brazier built into the base.

Hand- and foot-warming devices, common in the U.S. and Europe before central heating, also included braziers, usually a perforated sheet-metal box carried in a wooden frame. Early colonists rested their feet on these in church, perhaps with a quilt over the lap to hold in the heat.

The traditional Japanese house lacks central heating, it being an extravagance in that frugal society to warm space when only the body needs heat. Braziers often provided the heat, along with excruciatingly hot baths. The *kotatsu* is a pit in the floor of the room with a low table set over it and a quilt draped over the table. People sit at the table with their legs dangling and the quilt over all, warmed

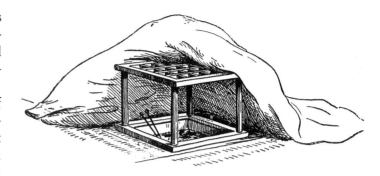

Figure 49   Bedclothes warm over a charcoal fire in a nineteenth-century Japanese inn. The fire is recessed in a pit in the floor.

by a brazier in the pit below. Similar devices appear in China and Iran, the Iranians sometimes using a pipe embedded in the floor to blow the coals into life. In Japan today, the brazier has been replaced by an electric heater.

The Japanese traditionally used braziers to warm their beds as well, the beds being quilts placed on the floor at night and put away by day. Edward S. Morse described a night spent in a nineteenth-century Japanese inn where each room contained a small hole in the floor designed to hold a charcoal fire. Wooden frames were erected over the holes, and the bedclothes draped over these. Morse found that this created a warm nest to sleep in, useful also by day when "one may gather a portion of the bedclothes about him and keep warm by a little coal fire burning beneath."

In modern times the Japanese brazier has invaded the U.S., in the form of the hibachi, for outdoor cooking use.

Very large braziers, sometimes several feet in diameter, heated churches and other public buildings in Europe into modern times. Trinity College, Cambridge, used one until the mid-nineteenth century. Braziers warmed the House of Commons in London as late as 1791. Today, of course, people who buy braziers to broil meat are warned never to use them indoors because of danger from fumes, notably carbon monoxide. What of the past, when millions used them indoors? The answer seems to be much the same as with the automobile: It is great if used correctly; mistakes can be fatal. A contemporary found the air in the House of Commons "pernicious in the extreme" because of braziers. There is no doubt at all that many people were overcome and died during the brazier era; various classical authors comment on it.

One experimenter concluded, quite reasonably, that braziers were dangerous chiefly in small, tightly closed rooms. Since houses in moderate climates are often airy, braziers could be safely used in them. But I suspect it boils down to this: The ancients knew very well how to use braziers safely. Nevertheless individuals sometimes failed to do so; they did not bother, or had too much wine and forgot, and so died. Much the same might be said today of automobile drivers, or wood-stove users.

The ruins of Pompeii contained some braziers more sophisticated than most. Some had hollow metal walls in which water circulated and was warmed. Others had hollow grates through which water was piped. A third type had vents that let air in at the base of the fire, improving combustion. It is a short step from these Pompeiian braziers to the closed iron stove. The metal container is there, sometimes enclosed completely. The grate is present, and the vent for combustion air. All that's needed is the chimney, a connecting pipe, and a door for fuel.

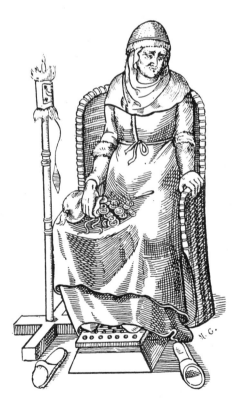

Figure 50 Woman using brazier designed as foot warmer. France, sixteenth century.

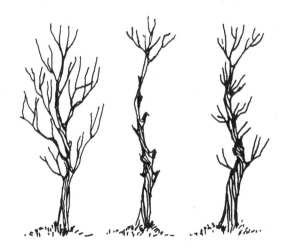

Chapter 4

The First Energy Crisis

But what need is there to speak of quantity?
Are not the mountains seen to be covered with trees,
the valleys full, and the plains occupied? Do not wild
trees outnumber even the leaves of domesticated ones,
and the areas occupied by trees exceed perhaps those
that are free?

Vannoccio Biringuccio,
The Pirotechnia, 1540.

At the end of the tenth century, Europe north of the Mediterranean was heavily forested. Wood was the essential fuel and for the most part there was plenty of it. Five hundred years later, quite suddenly in historical terms, complaints about the price and availability of wood increased; books began to appear on wood-conserving stoves. What might be called the first energy crisis, precursor of events in our own day, had begun in Europe.

The causes of this development were complex. Certainly conditions were not everywhere the same; there were areas of fuel abundance as well as areas of scarcity. It won't do to say simply that there was a wood shortage. Yet people were concerned, then as now; something vital in their world had begun to shift about; there were cries and alarms. Today month by month and year by year, we make adjustments in our lives having to do with energy, adjustments that a few years ago we were not making. Something very like that began to happen in Europe four hundred years ago.

Perhaps the most important factor was population growth, that and the increasing concentration of people in towns. During the Middle Ages in Europe trade and the growth of towns proceeded hand in hand. There was a new way of life in the towns, more trade, more commerce, more manufacturing. Surplus people from the countryside flowed into the towns to take part. Demand for wood, once as well-dispersed as the rural population, began to concentrate in densely settled areas. The drain on woodlands around those areas became heavier. The fact that roads and transport were then relatively poor probably contributed. The farther wood travels, the more expensive it gets. Wood can be reduced to charcoal and then transported as lighter and more concentrated energy, and this was done in the past. But turning wood into charcoal was not inexpensive, either. Even today, transporting wood fuel more than thirty miles or so is considered by some to be too expensive; imagine the situation before paved roads, trucks, or railroads. Floating logs down a river was economical, but it was not everywhere possible. So the price of wood went up and in some areas there were surely real shortages.

It is important to understand that four hundred years ago wood was *the* source of fuel, to a degree greater than with oil today. Now we have alternatives in coal, gas, nuclear energy, wood, and so on. Four hundred years ago, every industry dependent on fire needed wood or its byproduct, charcoal. You needed wood to smelt iron, to make glass, to brew beer, to fire kilns that made brick, tile, pottery, or lime for plaster and mortar. A single London glassmaker of that era might have burned seventy cords of wood a month. During the sixteenth century London's brewers burned twenty thousand wagonloads of wood per year. Then there was wood for construction—four thousand oaks for Windsor Castle alone; another four thousand for each major warship in the Royal Navy. There was wood for cooking and heating, all of it consumed in open fires or stoves of very low efficiency.

In England between 1086 and 1346, the population tripled. Numbers grew on the Continent as well. This meant more timber for building, and wood for heating, manufacturing, and cooking. Above all, perhaps, in terms of the destruction of woodlands, it meant clearing land to grow crops so the new population could be fed. In continental Europe as in England, this seems to have caused the greatest amount of permanent forest clearance.

In the year 1230, England began to import timber from Norway. During one hundred fifty years ending about 1610, the price of wood rose 266 percent in London. On the Continent prices rose too. Wood was so expensive in northern France during the thirteenth century that the poor used rented coffins to carry their dead, returning them after the body was placed in the grave.

In winter, before the modern age, activity virtually ceased; everything came to a halt. Pierre Riché, in his description of Charlemagne's era, offered an illuminating quotation from the *Annales de Fulda* of the ninth century: "This year winter was so hard that we could not get wood for heating, and nearly a third of the people died." At that time, according to Riché, "great quantities of wood were required from the peasants to feed the fires in palaces and abbeys."

At first the concern over European

fuel supplies was spotty and local; concern spread in the sixteenth through the eighteenth centuries. The elements of the situation were the same as in our own day: fuel supply in question, prices rising, society feeling threatened. Individuals and governments began to seek ways to conserve fuel. They built more efficient heating systems; in time they developed new sources of energy, notably coal.

COPPICE AND POLLARD

Among the early approaches to fuel conservation, now long forgotten but worthy of recall, were the practices of coppicing and pollarding. The word *coppice* is a form of copse, meaning a patch of small trees or bushes. In the past coppice had a broader meaning; it referred to a patch of woodland specifically managed and cropped, or to the practice of managing woodland in this way. Coppice wood had a variety of uses in construction, woodworking, agriculture, and as fuel. The practice of coppicing involves cutting the tree close to or at ground level, and then encouraging sprouts to grow from the stump. After a few years, when the sprouts have become poles of suitable size, they are cut. This is done on a regular rotation—seven years, ten years, a dozen years, depending on the species of tree, or the use to which the poles will be put, and on the speed with which they grow.

There is evidence of coppicing in Stone Age Britain, five thousand to six thousand years ago. According to Oliver Rackham, who has written extensively about ancient woodland practices, "Prehistoric men observed that the regrowth of shoots from a stump were more useful than the original tree; they developed woodland management not as a conservation measure but to supply sizes and quantities of wood not easily to be got from wildwood." In the days of stone tools, it made sense to encourage wood to grow in the required sizes and shapes, rather than cut it to shape with a stone axe.

The Romans maintained coppice woods in Britain, managing many thousands of acres in this way to support their iron industry. In Britain and on the Continent coppicing was widely used through the Middle Ages and thereafter. It has continued to some extent right into the twentieth century, though in modern times on a much smaller and declining scale. One great advantage of the coppice system is the vast root structure, sometimes centuries old, which supports the sprouts growing from a stump. These sprouts may, in the right conditions, grow ten feet in a year. After each crop of poles is cut the root system remains in place to feed new growth. Contrast this with a new approach to forestry in the industrial age: The machine that can wrench up an entire tree, feed it into an iron maw and reduce stump, trunk, roots, and branches to wood chips in a matter of moments. In the process the forest floor is torn up so that erosion can take place; new trees must be planted or

Figure 51   Late medieval Flemish woodland scene, showing (beyond hunters and fallen boar) a coppice cut on regular rotation. The wood was used for fuel and other purposes. Some larger trees in foreground appear to have had the lower branches removed, perhaps for fodder.

Figure 53 Pollard trees appear often in illustrations for medieval manuscripts. Here ladies hunt rabbits, or perhaps each other, amongst the pollards.

Figure 52 Pollard trees (bottom) were cut well above ground level. In a coppice (middle drawings) trees were cut approximately at ground level. Shredding (top drawings) was the practice of removing branches from standing trees, for fuel or fodder.

seeded, and these will take many years to establish substantial growth. One seventeenth-century British estimate suggests that wood production in the coppice is one-third greater than in ordinary timberland.

The poles harvested from a coppice are easier to handle than big timber; they require no heavy equipment for handling, no splitting for fuel use. In the past a specific type of coppice might be maintained primarily for a particular use—cooking, heating fuel, fencing, charcoal for a foundry. Used in this way, wood supplies regenerated in a more real sense perhaps than today, when we use the term "renewable resource" rather casually and without real reference to whether we are in fact replacing what we use.

Many a contemporary American, including myself, has been puzzled in Europe to see long rows of trees cut off

eight to twelve feet above the ground. From the stump tops, like arboreal headdresses, grow sprouts and later poles which in time get trimmed back to the stump. Whence came this outlandish practice, this mutilation? Today trees may be trimmed like this purely for decorative purposes in parks. But originally it was a question of fuel, or fodder. The cutoff trees are called pollards.

The coppice trunk is cut, as noted, close to the ground. But when sprouts come up, it is essential to fence livestock out of the coppice. Otherwise they will eat the sprouts. Thus grew up the practice of pollarding, of cutting off trees sufficiently high up so that stock could not reach the sprouts. In woodland pasture, along roads, around farmyards—wherever trees grew that could not readily be protected from stock—pollard trees appear. The purpose is the same as with the coppice, except that you need a ladder to harvest the poles. The leaves from these poles are sometimes used as feed for animals. Providing fodder without destroying the tree seems to have been an important function of the coppice as well in the past. So was the practice of shredding, or removing branches from a woodland tree except for a tuft at the top; leaves gathered in this way became feed both for livestock and for deer in the parks.

FIRE AS THREAT

A wood supply that was dwindling, or less accessible or higher priced, offered an excuse to improve heating. Safety was certainly another factor. As towns grew in density and size, space was at a premium. Multistoried buildings came into demand and one was built right against the next. A fire in one structure threatened many, and the accompanying table suggests what the price could be. But the table hits only a few highlights; the loss of villages and small towns did not make historical headlines.

Open-hearth fires remained widely in use in Europe into the nineteenth century. But where dense settlement occurred, regulations began to restrict and control fire use long before. As early as the thirteenth century in Norway, an ordinance for the town of Bergen provided that no new stove or oven could be fired unless inspected and approved by town authorities. Curfew became widely prac-

Great Fires in History

In the wood-burning era fire destroyed whole villages, towns, and cities with a regularity that we have, in the modern era, all but forgotten. The following is a partial listing of cities destroyed by fire as carried in the *Encyclopedia Britannica*, eleventh edition, New York, 1910:

Year	City	Estimate of Loss
798	London	Nearly destroyed.
982	London	Greater part of city burned.
1086	London	All houses and churches from east to west gates burned.
1212	London	Greater part of the city burned.
1666	London	The Great Fire burned from Sept. 2–6, destroying 13,200 houses and many other buildings.
1137	York	Totally destroyed.
1507	Norwich	Nearly destroyed.
1700	Edinburgh	The Great Fire.
1612	Cork	Greater part burned; again in 1622.
1613	Dorchester	Nearly destroyed.
1614	Stratford-on-Avon	Burned.
1875	Glasgow	Great Fire.
64	Rome	Burned for eight days; 10 of 14 wards destroyed.
1106	Venice	Greater part of city burned.
1405	Bern	Destroyed.
1491	Dresden	Destroyed.
1842	Hamburg	Fire rages May 5–7; 2000 dwellings destroyed.
1541	Aarhus, Denmark	Almost destroyed; again in 1556.
1702	Bergen	Greater part of town destroyed.
1728	Copenhagen	Nearly destroyed; again in 1795.
1751	Stockholm	1,000 houses destroyed.
1736	St. Petersburg	2,000 houses burn.
1752	Moscow	18,000 houses burn.
1812	Moscow	Russians fire the city to drive out Napoleon; fire burns five days and destroys nine-tenths of the city, 30,800 houses.

1729	Constantinople	12,000 houses burned, 7,000 people lost.
1745	Constantinople	Fire lasts five days.
1750	Constantinople	10,000 houses burn.
1756	Constantinople	15,000 houses burn.
1782	Constantinople	10,000 houses burn.
1791	Constantinople	32,000 houses burn; as many again in 1795.
1822	Canton	Nearly destroyed.
1866	Yokohama	Two-thirds destroyed.
1872	Yeddo	Six square miles destroyed.
1873	Yeddo	10,000 houses destroyed.
1796	Charleston, S.C.	300 houses burn.
1838	Charleston, S.C.	Half the city burned.
1802	Portsmouth, N.H.	102 buildings destroyed.
1813	Portsmouth, N.H.	397 buildings destroyed.
1820	Savannah	463 buildings burned.
1835	New York	The Great Fire burned 52 acres.
1845	Pittsburgh	Large part of city burned.
1846	Nantucket	Almost destroyed.
1848	Albany, N.Y.	One-third of city burned, 600 houses lost.
1851	St. Louis	Three-fourths of city burned.
1850	Philadelphia	400 buildings burned.
1851	San Francisco	2,500 buildings burned.
1871	Chicago	The Great Fire, Oct. 8–10, burned 2,124 acres in the heart of the city, taking 250 lives and destroying 17,430 buildings; 98,500 homeless.
1862	Troy, N.Y.	Nearly destroyed.
1866	Portland, Me.	Half the city burned; 50 buildings blown up to halt the fire.
1845	Quebec	1,650 houses burned.
1866	Quebec	2,500 houses burned.
1877	St. John, N.B.	1,650 dwellings lost.
1852	Montreal	Fire makes 10,000 homeless.
1862	Valparaiso	Destroyed.

ticed in Europe, not to get everyone into bed at a given hour, but to contain fire. The purpose was to see that fires were extinguished or covered so that the town remained safe during the night hours. Watchtowers were widely used. "Owing to the wooden tiles with which the houses are commonly roofed in Hungary," John Paget wrote one hundred thirty years ago, "the danger of fire is very great; and in almost every town, a watchman is consequently employed to give the alarm, and as a sign of his vigilance he is obliged to blow a shrill whistle every quarter of an hour, day and night."

Various regions had their own means of dealing with the fire risk. Moscow, much of which burned on more than one occasion, used watchtowers. Saunas were once forbidden there in summer, except for the aristocracy. Lithuanians, among others, often kept ladders permanently fixed to the roof to provide access if the thatch caught fire. I am told that the distinctive shallow roof pitch in Switzerland stems from old regulations aimed at making it easier for firefighters to work on the roof. The Chinese long ago learned to divide their cities into districts separated by very wide avenues. These acted as firebreaks to prevent flames from spreading from district to district, and perhaps engulfing the entire city. In Rome the Emperor Augustus built a one hundred and fifteen foot fire wall to protect his forum from fires that often swept a nearby tenement district.

Figure 54 Japanese *kura*. Note thickness of clay doors.

With their characteristic light frame structures and paper walls, Japanese cities were particularly susceptible to fire. The more prosperous citizens, and many shops, maintained fireproof structures where they could store valuables and take refuge themselves if fire swept the town. The fireproof structure, known as a *kura*, had thick walls and doors built of clay and plaster. Normally the family did not live in the *kura*, but retreated to it when fire threatened. Edward S. Morse described the scene from nineteenth-century Japan:

In the city one may notice a little platform or staging with handrail erected on the ridge of the roof; a ladder or flight of steps leads to this staging, and on alarms of fire anxious faces may be seen peering from these lookouts in the direction of the burning buildings. It is usual to have resting on the platform a huge bucket or half barrel filled with water, and near by a long-handled brush; and this is used to sprinkle water on places threatened by sparks and firebrands, which often fill the air in times of great conflagrations.

During the prevalence of a high wind it is a common sight to see the small dealers packing their goods in large baskets and square cloths to tie up ready to transport in case of fire. At such times the windows and doors of the *kura* are closed and the chinks plastered with mud, which is always at hand either under a platform near the door or in a large earthen jar near the openings. In private dwellings, too, at times of possible danger, the more precious objects are packed up in a square basket-like box, having straps attached to it, so that it can easily be transported on one's shoulders.

Figure 55 Water tub and brush stood on the roof of this nineteenth-century Japanese house in case of fire.

In the modern era we lack the preoccupation, the deeply embedded fear of fire that some of our ancestors came to know. Most of us remain at the euphoric stage of the return to wood burning: happy that the stove works, happy that it heats the house, happy that it offers a measure of independence from oil, gas, and electric heat. Questions of safety have barely begun to surface. Fire departments and insurance companies are increasingly aware that such questions exist and in abundance.

Northern Lights

Many witnesses, including visiting foreigners, have described the unforgettable and characteristic look of the winter landscape in northern Sweden during olden times, when smoke and flame issued from the minaret-like chimneys as though spurting from a blast furnace. An English clergyman traveling in Småland remarked that: "The only wood plentifully available here is pine. In the cottages there is always an oven with a huge fire burning in it, in spite of which you feel chilly in the room even while moving nearer to the stove. The sparks fly around the chimney so that each cottage can be seen from a distance when you travel by night. For safety, the roofs are covered with turf which, being damp from snow or rain, will not catch fire."

Sigurd Erixon, "Spjället, en Exponent För Svensk Bostadsteknik," *Svenska Kulturbilder*, Stockholm, 1937

In the course of time losses from fire brought a turn away from wooden construction in Europe. It was not simply that good timber was harder to find; there was an interest in masonry buildings for the sake of safety. In London Richard I ordered a switch from timber to masonry construction to reduce fire hazards. In Oxford a similar change came after a fire that destroyed much of the town in 1190. Wooden floors in England were sometimes overlaid with mortar as a safety measure.

Figure 56 Early efforts to diminish fire risk included the development of spark hoods. Some, such as this Hungarian model, channeled smoke into the attic.

Figure 57 Sheltering the entire kitchen area under a masonry vault also reduced fire risk. Smoke still poured through the house, but sparks were caught under the vault. This example is from Hungary.

In thickly settled areas of the central Alps in Switzerland, open hearths were prohibited in the seventeenth century. In 1610 every home owner in St. Moritz was threatened with a fine if he did not have a kitchen vault (to protect against sparks) and a chimney by Michaelmas. In 1692 St. Moritz required that chimneys be built five spans above the roof, and that they be carefully cleaned. The community of Tschlin required chimneys as of 1732, along with spark-protection vaults in the kitchen. In what is now Germany we know of a police order from the time of the Thirty Years War (1618) requiring fire walls be built on either side of open hearths set against the wall. Thus the open hearths were protected at the back and on each side; they were open now only at the front and above. The next step was the clay vault to arch above the open fire, to block the rise of sparks. The final step, in a pattern that occurred across Europe, was the erection of a chimney, which carried the smoke outdoors.

In England the shift from fireplace to chimney began after the Norman conquest, the Normans presumably bringing this useful idea with them from the Continent. It has also been suggested that the Normans, being a minority in a hostile land, wanted to be up on second stories and battlements, where they could look down upon hostile natives. Because building second stories was problematic with open fires below, the solution was to shove the fire over against a sidewall, trap its smoke and vent it to the outdoors along with 90 percent of the heat.

Having arrived at this solution, the Normans began to build it into manor houses. The idea spread slowly to the country's cottages, but by the sixteenth century chimneys were general in villages where they had been uncommon a generation before. The same gradual shift occurred throughout Europe, though the time scale varied. The chimney was known as early as the ninth century in Switzerland (St. Gall), but came into more general use only centuries later.

THE FIRST ENERGY CRISIS 51

THE LITTLE ICE AGE

Several hundred years ago, then, two factors began to affect the design of heating systems in Europe: One was concern about the wood supply, or about its cost. The other was safety. And the solution to the safety question, the chimney, was capable of removing 90 percent of the heat from the house. Now a third factor must be added: climate. Between 1550 and 1850 there was a period of extreme cold in Europe. Modern investigators call it the Little Ice Age. Most of the outcry about fuel supplies, and a flood of innovations in heating-system design, occur within this period. At the beginning of the period in 1550, all Europe heated with open fires, braziers, or simple stoves and ovens of very low efficiency. By the end of the period, well-designed stoves had appeared in virtually every country. Many crude designs remained in use, especially in rural areas, but excellent designs were available. Some modern versions of these designs remain among the best available today.

Fernand Braudel has written of "the continual rain, the disastrous floods, the bitter and *unusual* cold" at the end of the sixteenth century. In Vol. I of *The Mediterranean* he remarks that "In 1575, in the Rumanian countryside, which was normally rich in cereals, the flocks died by the hundred; the birds were surprised in March by snowdrifts five feet deep and could be caught in the hand. As for the human inhabitants, they would kill their neighbors for a piece of bread." Not every year, of course, was as bad. Winters varied then as now. But the grip of cold was harsher, more persistent than it had been, and people suffered from it.

The typical stove of the sixteenth century, at the start of the Little Ice Age, was little better than a fireplace in terms of efficiency. Alfred Faber, a German historian of heating technology, has estimated the efficiency of typical stoves at that time as 20 to 30 percent. The early clay or tile models were probably especially poor. They lacked any sort of baffle or channel system to hold heat in the stove. When such stoves were hooked to a chimney, the heat departed very rapidly. Add to that the fact that it was difficult for heat to penetrate the thick walls of these stoves, and you have a fairly wretched device.

People at the time were not unaware of the problem. Where the crude clay oven was *not* hooked to a chimney, its heat remained in the dwelling, as it had with the open fire. And so in Russia as the chimney came into use, the same house might harbor two types of stove: the "white" stove hooked to the chimney, and the "black" stove pouring its smoke into the room. The black stove was for serious heating; the white stove for use when heat did not matter so much.

The Chinese have the honor of producing the first cast-iron stoves, around 220 A.D. But they never did much with the idea thereafter. Europeans began to

Figure 58 North German jamb stove, with drying rack for clothing on top. The stove was fueled through a stokehole in the sidewall (or jamb) of the fireplace, located in the adjoining room. Just above the stokehole another opening carried smoke from the jamb stove into the fireplace chimney. Figure 42 shows the location of a jamb stove fueled from a walk-in chimney.

make cast-iron stoves in the fifteenth century. These were crude devices, low in efficiency, but they did have one advantage over the old clay and tile stoves: better heat transfer. During its brief sojourn in the iron stove, the heat had a better opportunity to get out into the room through the cast-iron wall than it did through the thick clay wall. The iron wall was thinner, and transferred heat better. So early cast-iron models did have an advantage. Some of these reached America, where they were known as jamb stoves because of the fact that they were fueled through the jamb or sidewall of the fireplace; you simply shoveled coals, embers, or whatever out of the fireplace and into the iron firebox to heat an adjacent room. Early cast-iron plates were also used to form the back wall of a fireplace, and thus to transmit heat to an adjoining room.

According to Alfred Faber, the great innovations in stove design during this period seldom came from specialists in the field. The guilds prevented this, standing guard over old ways. "Every invention which transcended the limited sphere of the craft was combatted and regarded with distrust." Change represented a threat to traditional guild power, so the masons, potters, and metalworkers held to the old ways. "Homeowners," Faber found, "often experimented for years on their own stoves to reduce wood consumption. Their discoveries have appeared in hundreds of reports, books and journals. Among

them almost all professions are represented: government officials, priests, monks, doctors, pharmacists, mathematicians, professors of all fields, but also painters, architects, merchants, manufacturers, diplomats, military men . . ."*

It is curious, and perhaps not just a coincidence, that the first patent for a wood-conserving stove came in 1557, just seven years after the beginning of the Little Ice Age. The patent went to a citizen of Strasbourg in what is now France. The stove itself was said to cost more than a year's supply of firewood. In 1564 in Alsace one Peter Schmidt produced a small picture book showing "new stoves for the conservation of wood." All were tile stoves, three for heating, the others for cooking, roasting, or baking. In 1582 a citizen of Nürnberg got a patent for "the useful art of conserving wood" in firing systems. And so it went, over much of northern Europe.

In 1618 one Franz Kessler, an artist and inventor from Cologne, published a book on wood-conserving stoves, including both iron and tile models. In 1763 Frederick the Great of Prussia staged a competition for "a room stove which would consume the least wood." The government of Sweden set out in 1767 to sponsor improved stove designs; so did the Economic Welfare Society of Denmark in 1796. Even in Norway, with

*From Alfred Faber, *1000 Jahre Werdegang von Herd und Ofen*. Abhandlungen und Berichte, Vol. 18. Deutsches Museum, Munich, 1950.

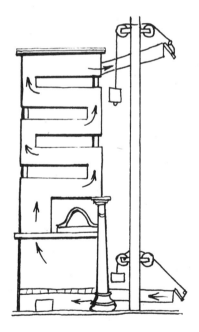

Figures 59 and 60   Two wood-conserving stove designs by Franz Kessler of Cologne, circa 1618.

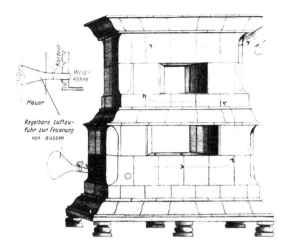

Figure 61 Stove designed by I. P. Baumer in 1764. It won Frederick the Great's contest for improved design. Baumer's approach is still in use today in some Scandinavian stoves. Courtesy of Deutsches Museum.

its vast forests and small population, in the mid-1700s foresters were urging the design of stoves to save wood. But Norway specialized in wood-conserving *iron* stoves, and produced many of them.

According to Faber, Franz Kessler was the first to use baffles to force smoke into a slower and more circuitous path within the stove, so that it gave up its heat before reaching the chimney. This has remained a major technique for improving efficiency. There is nothing terribly complex or difficult about it, and the technique remains the same whether one is dealing with stoves made of iron, brick, tile, or mud. All you do is keep the hot gases in the stove until they have cooled; then you let them out. Today in a mason-

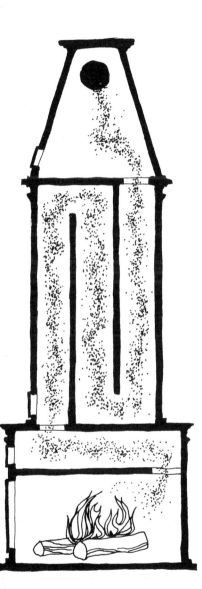
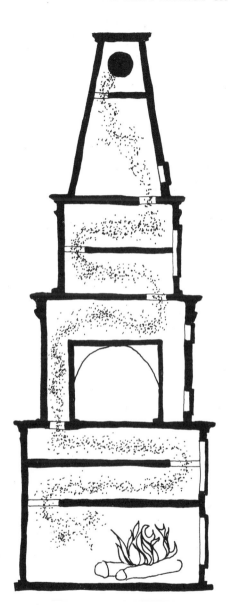

Figures 62 and 63 These Norwegian cast-iron stoves, dating from around 1800, used lengthy smoke paths and a large radiating surface to improve efficiency.

Figure 64 (top) and 65 (bottom) American foundries also began to turn out more efficient stoves in the nineteenth century, using longer smoke paths and more radiating surface. The dumb stove (bottom) was an American device that sat on the second floor of the house. Smoke from a stove situated in the room below passed through the dumb stove, losing much of its heat. (Collections of Greenfield Village and The Henry Ford Museum.)

ry stove, smoke winds through a series of channels or passages, losing heat to the masonry as it goes. The basic principle is just the same as it was in Kessler's time, but it has been refined through three hundred fifty years of experience.

Once the idea of baffles and smoke passages got about, many experimented with them and in ways of almost infinite variety. During the following centuries, smoke made its way along paths both circuitous and tortured through stoves of all shapes and sizes—round stoves, square stoves, tall stoves, squat stoves, columned stoves, iron stoves, tile stoves, clay stoves, even stoves in the shape of a peasant woman or of the Bastille. It is almost fair to say that if you can imagine a stove, and if you can imagine a winding smoke path within it, then someone, at some time in the past, has already built it. The stoves shown in these pages offer a broad sampling, but only a sampling.

It is an irony that after some three hundred years of intense effort at improving wood-stove design, the "solution" to the first energy crisis turned out to be coal. Just as wood-burning methods reached a pinnacle, coal cut the ground out from under them in the 1800s. Then came oil, gas, and electricity to finish the job. Now, late in the twentieth century, it looks as though wood burning's time has come again—not as *the* solution to the second energy crisis, but as one of the solutions. Some of the old methods are being looked at once more, and with a new respect. Most of

the wood stoves being mass-marketed today are but pale reflections of better designs that flourished sixty to a hundred years ago, and that one hopes may flourish again.

Figure 66   Picasso sits next to a French coal stove with an impressive heat exchanger. 1939 photo by Brassai. Courtesy of the Worcester Art Museum, Worcester, Mass.

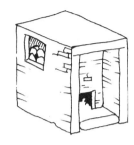

Figure 67   In Estonia the sauna stove evolved from a rock pile to an enclosed masonry structure with rocks inside it. Drying kilns followed a very similar evolution, gaining not only in safety but also in heat storage capacity and probably in efficiency.

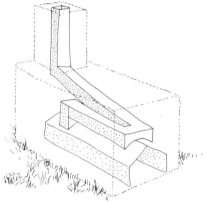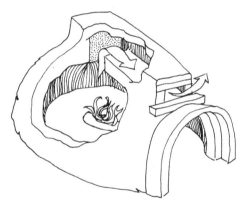

Figures 68 and 69   The internal flue passages in these Finnish baking ovens were designed to improve both draft and heating within the oven. The pattern suggests ways in which masonry stove heating techniques may have developed.

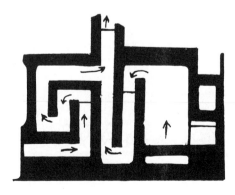

Figure 70   Flue patterns of two masonry heating stoves of an early type, from the east Baltic area. The stoves are back to back in separate rooms, feeding smoke into a central chimney. The lines across flues represent dampers.

Fireplace Improvements

Inventors also turned their attention to the fireplace during the first energy crisis. In 1624 Louis Savot described the use in France of air circulation systems within a fireplace, much as in the Heatilator of today. Ducts carried room air into an enclosed space behind the fire to be warmed, then recirculated it into the room. Savot also noted the use of an iron plate, a kind of fire back, as the rear wall of the fireplace. The other side of the plate warmed an adjacent room. In 1678 Prince Rupert, Duke of Bavaria, installed a baffle system behind the grate of his own fireplace. The idea was to slow the passage of smoke and heat up the chimney and so gain more warmth in the room. During the eighteenth century, Nicholas Gauger in France devised a system, more elaborate than Savot's, for ducting room air behind the fire to be warmed. Benjamin Franklin later became familiar with the work of both Prince Rupert and Gauger. In America he combined their ideas in his own fireplace design, but it doesn't seem to have worked very well. Few of the original Franklins were ever made. Instead, somewhat later, the stove industry attached the Franklin name to a device Franklin never had anything to do with, a simple iron fireplace with doors that open and shut. Another American, Benjamin Thompson of Woburn, Massachusetts, had a more powerful and lasting influence on fireplace and chimney design. Alas, he has never been a hero in his native land because he fled to England during the Revolution. In England Thompson won the title Count Rumford. His contributions to chimney and fireplace design were substantial, though he added no ducts or baffles. His fireplaces remain superior today, though at present they are seldom built.

Figure 71 Prince Rupert's fireplace attempted to slow the passage of smoke up the chimney and thus to save heat.

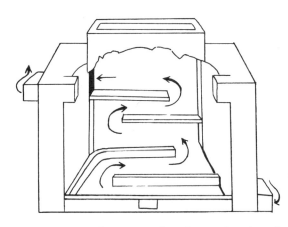

Figure 72 Gauger's fireplace circulated room air through passages beneath and behind the fire, thus warming the air.

Figure 73 Franklin's fireplace attempted to combine the approaches used by Prince Rupert and Gauger.

Stove Efficiency, Circa 1820

Stove efficiency tests today tell us little that was not known long ago to experimenters like Marcus Bull. Bull's tests in England in the 1820s showed that: fireplace efficiency is extremely poor; Franklin stove performance is better but still poor; efficiency improves dramatically as smoke is made to follow a longer and longer path from firebox to chimney, giving up heat as it travels. Good stove designers used this knowledge long before Bull. But they built the long smoke channels into the stove instead of using stovepipe, as Bull did.

Bull's tests (see his results in the table) involved heating a special room with various stoves, and with different lengths of stovepipe. The figures in column one, given in hours, can also be read as comparative efficiency ratings, with apparatus number 9 representing 100 percent. Fireplace efficiency would then be 10 percent, Franklin stoves 37 percent, and so on. Apparatus number 4 at 45 percent comes closest to the typical box stove of today. Numbers 6 and 7, with their long smoke paths and ratings of 78 percent and 82 percent, compare closely with typical advanced masonry stoves from north, east, and central Europe. Modern experimenters, testing stoves today, get results similar to Bull's on efficiency.

Marcus Bull's Test Results*

No.	Description of the Apparatus Used	Time the room was maintained at the same temperature in the combustion of equal weights of fuel compared with apparatus No. 9.	Weight of fuel required by each apparatus to maintain the room the same time and temperature compared with No. 9.
1	CHIMNEY FIREPLACE, of ordinary construction for burning wood	10	1000
2	OPEN PARLOR GRATE, of ordinary construction for burning anthracite coal	18	555
3	OPEN FRANKLIN STOVE, with one elbow joint and 5 feet of 6-inch pipe placed vertically, the fireplace being closed with a fire board	37	270
4	CAST-IRON TEN-PLATE STOVE, with one elbow joint and 5 feet of 4-inch pipe placed horizontally, entering the fire board	45	222
5	SHEET-IRON CYLINDER STOVE, the interior surface coated with clay lute, with one elbow joint and 5 feet of 2-inch pipe placed horizontally, entering the fire board	67	149
6	SHEET-IRON CYLINDER STOVE, as before described, with three elbow joints, 4½ feet and 9 feet of 2-inch pipe, the whole placed as follows: 3½ feet horizontally, 5 feet vertically, for an ascending current, and 5 feet vertically for a descending current, entering the fire board	78	128
7	SHEET-IRON CYLINDER STOVE, as before described, with three elbow joints, 4½ feet and 9 feet of 2-inch pipe, placed as follows: 9 inches vertically and 12¾ feet horizontally entering the fire board	82	122
8	SHEET-IRON CYLINDER STOVE, as before described, with nine elbow joints, measuring 13½ feet of 2-inch pipe, entering the fire board	95	105
9	SHEET-IRON CYLINDER STOVE, as before described, with 42 feet of 2-inch pipe, as used in the course of experiments on fuel	100	100

*From *Experiments to Determine the Comparative Quantities of Heat Evolved in the Combustion of Principal Varieties of Wood and Coal Used in the U.S. for Fuel*, by Marcus Bull, Transactions of the American Philosophical Society, III, (new series), Philadelphia, 1830.

PART
2

PRACTICAL MATTERS

Although all masters have the same objective, each one proceeds to make this kind of furnace according to his own ideas so that it can be said that there are almost as many different shapes of such furnaces as there are masters.

Vannoccio Biringuccio, *The Pirotechnica*, 1540.

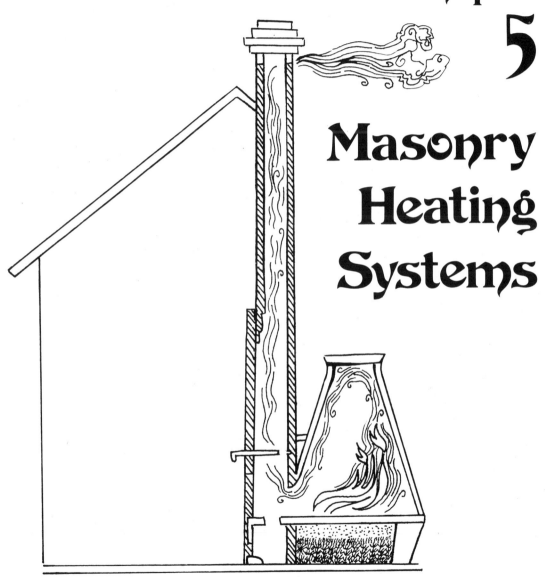

Chapter 5

Masonry Heating Systems

asonry heating systems differ in important ways, according to climate, building tradition, fuel, and function. One kind of system may serve the bath, another the kitchen or living area. Cold climates demand one sort of stove, moderate climates another. Wood has been the common fuel, but there are areas of Europe where the only fuel has been grass or reeds.

Terms can be confusing, so let me explain how I've used the term "masonry stove." Some stoves are fired with the fuel door closed. Others may be fired with the door (or doors) open; then the stove looks like what North Americans would think of as a fireplace, as in Figure 110. I've used the term "masonry stove" to refer both to closed-door models and to fireplace-stoves. A masonry stove *can* do double duty as a fireplace, though probably with some loss in efficiency when operating in the open door mode.

In Europe today masonry stoves that burn wood tend to be known as stoves for intermittent firing. That is, they are fired for short periods once or twice a day. That is the traditional way. Masonry stoves that burn coal or coke are called often continuous combustion stoves; they burn all the time, like our iron stoves.

In the following chapters, I have separated traditional masonry stoves into four categories:

1. Systems that provide heat beneath the floor: including the Afghan *tawakhaneh*, Roman hypocaust, Chinese k'ang, Korean ondol and German steinofen.

2. East European stoves, including Russian, Polish, Hungarian, Rumanian, Lithuanian, Latvian, Estonian, and Finnish models.

3. Swedish stoves.

4. Central European stoves including Swiss, Austrian and, German models.

Baking ovens and cooking ranges constitute a fifth category, but one so large as to merit a separate book.

The categories are somewhat arbitrary, but they reflect a basic structural reality. In some countries—Poland, Hungary, Finland, and others—varied traditions meet and mix. Historians have not sorted all this out. Perhaps they never will; perhaps it is not essential that they do. Real and important differences in building style do exist, and we'll get to these in due course. First it would be worthwhile to consider some of the things that masonry stoves have in common.

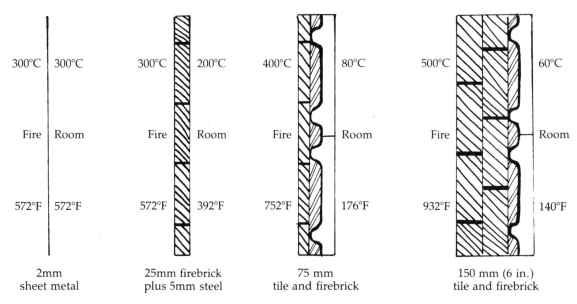

Figure 74 This illustration shows how temperature varies inside and outside the stove with changes in wall thickness. Fireclay transfers heat forty times more slowly than iron of the same thickness. Drawing courtesy of *Informationsstelle Kachelofen*, Stuttgart.

62

HEAT STORAGE

Masonry stoves are heat-storage systems. Heat built rapidly in the firebox is stored in the masonry body of the stove, and then released slowly to the room. In this way a masonry stove achieves even and steady heat output over a long period of time. It contrasts with the iron stove, which achieves even heat output by slowing combustion, by starving the fire for air.

The greater the mass of a masonry stove, the more heat it can store. From a single firing lasting only two to four hours, the larger models (heavy or medium weight construction) may store enough warmth to heat a space for a day, or even longer. Generally, the designer will build in enough heat storage so that the stove need be fired only twice a day in the coldest weather.

A stove's mass depends in part on its outside dimensions, and in part on the thickness of its walls. Thin stove walls (the lightweight construction common in continuous combustion stoves) mean quick response; the warmth makes its way through the stove wall and out into the room more rapidly. Thick stove walls mean greater heat-storage capacity, but slower response. Several hours may pass from initial firing to the time when the stove's outer surface reaches peak temperature. Balancing the speed of response with heat-storage needs is an important element in masonry stove

Average Wall Thickness (cm)	Heat Output in Kilocalories per Hour per Square Meter (Kcal/hr/m^2)		Duration of Heat Storage in Hours until Completely Cold
	Intermittent Hot Fires	Continuous Combustion	
4	740	890	6
6	700	840	9
8	660	790	12
10	620	740	15
12	530	640	18

design. As with most other things in life, it is a question of finding and achieving the right balance.

Stoves in Europe are sometimes divided into categories according to their mass. Stoves of large thermal mass may weigh several tons; ten thousand pounds would not be exceptional in cold areas. Such stoves require special footings and foundation work just as a chimney or fireplace would, and normally they would be built on the ground floor of a building. Stoves of medium thermal mass might be in the fifteen hundred to three thousand pound range. These are more suitable for second-floor use, though with the same special support. Medium-mass stoves have in the past been manufactured in various countries, including

Finland and east Europe, with a sheet-metal covering over brick.

The table above shows the effect of masonry stove wall thickness on surface-heat output, and on the heat-storage capacity of the wall.

SURFACE TEMPERATURE

Leonidas Gimbutas, writing of masonry stoves in Lithuania in the 1920s, described both large- and medium-mass varieties. Then he listed a third category, stoves of small thermal mass made of cast iron. "Such stoves," he wrote, "burn dust or anything on their surface, and spoil the air with a bad smell. Recommended as temporary heating devices only." Dr. Gimbutas's advice is echoed by many who have had the opportunity to compare iron and masonry stoves.

Iron stoves get very hot. Surface temperatures of 400° or 500°F and higher are common, and the iron burns flesh at the touch. In the same way, any organic matter that settles on the stove in the form of dust will also burn. In time you'll detect the airborne residue of this frying dust (though you may not be aware of the cause) as a feeling of discomfort or irritation in the nose. The Soviet government has in the past considered this problem of such concern, for health reasons, that it set a limit on stove surface temperatures. Masonry stoves had to be designed so that surface temperatures would not exceed 80° to 90°C (176° to 194°F). Later the government relented a bit and permitted temperatures to rise to 120°C (248°F) for brief periods, so long as the *average* surface temperature did not go over 90°C.

This lore comes from a book written by L. A. Semenov and published in the U.S.S.R. in 1950. Whether the rules are in effect now I do not know, but it really doesn't matter. It all boils down to something that students of radiant heating have known for a long while: Low-level radiant heat is much the most comfortable form of heat to live with, and very likely it is also healthier. Masonry heating systems warm the room via a relatively large surface. Iron stoves use a relatively small but hot surface. The

differences, in terms of both safety and comfort, are clear.

HIGH-TEMPERATURE COMBUSTION

Manufacturers of iron stoves may warn against "overfiring" their products. By that they mean filling the stove with fuel, opening the draft wide, and letting the fire roar. Frequently then the stove will begin to glow red hot. Warping or other damage to metal parts may occur. Also, so much excess air moves through the stove, carrying heat away up the chimney, that efficiency drops sharply. There's a tall story from New England about the powerful drafts thus developed, including one so strong it sucked the stove right up the chimney.

Masonry stoves and ovens, however, are *designed* to be fired in this mode. What is poison for iron is meat and potatoes for the masonry model. The whole idea is to get ample oxygen well mixed with fuel in a firebox designed to promote good combustion. Not just any firebox shape or size will do for this, and the firebox must be lined with firebrick both as protection and to keep the heat in. Then temperatures will rise quickly above the level at which gases distilled from the wood will burn.

- The iron stove is designed to produce heat slowly and evenly, but to transmit the heat rapidly to the room. The fire smolders during long burns.

- The masonry stove is designed to produce heat rapidly, but to transmit it slowly to the room. The fire always burns quickly and at high temperature.

COMBUSTION EFFICIENCY

When anyone speaks of stove efficiency, two separate aspects are involved: combustion efficiency and heat-transfer efficiency.

Combustion efficiency involves effective burning: Are you developing all the heat potential in the fuel?

Heat-transfer efficiency involves getting the benefit of the heat. Is the heat being transferred effectively from stove to room? Efficient transfer means minimal loss up the chimney.

A well-designed stove must offer good heat transfer and good combustion. But efficiency depends only in part on design. The skill of the operator is also very important.

Now, consider combustion efficiency. Half to two-thirds of the fuel value of wood is locked up in gases and volatile liquids. These emerge from the wood as it is heated in the firebox. If they burn, combustion is good. If they do not burn, it is like throwing fuel away. Burning the gases requires temperatures in the 1,100° to 1,300°F range.

In the firebox of an ordinary iron stove, it is difficult to keep temperatures at levels that produce good combustion.

That is because the iron wall of the stove is so effective at transferring heat out of the firebox. Heat moves swiftly from the firebox to the room, and temperatures stay below good combustion levels. This is an inherent contradiction in the working of the iron firebox; it is self-defeating in terms of combustion efficiency. This shows up especially during long burns. The firebox is then loaded with fuel and the air supply is cut to slow and cool the fire. The result is unburned gases that show up as dense smoke output: air pollution. Another result is the buildup of soot and creosote in the chimney, with the risk of fire.

To grasp the dimensions of this problem in the iron stove, it is worth knowing that iron begins to glow red at temperatures above 900°F. That is still well below levels where complete combustion of wood gases occurs.

The masonry stove solves the problem by removing the contradiction. That is, it does not try to achieve high temperatures and heat transfer in the same location, the firebox. The masonry stove's firebox is lined with firebrick for insulation. The firebox is shaped to achieve and hold high temperatures and not to transfer heat. In a masonry stove firebox, temperatures should run several hundred degrees above the level necessary for complete combustion. You should see no smoke coming from the chimney, except during the brief period when the firebox warms as the fire starts. When wood combustion is complete, the only by-products (other than ash) are carbon dioxide and water vapor. You won't see anything coming from the chimney—no air pollution. Complete combustion also means no buildup of soot and creosote in the chimney.

HEAT TRANSFER EFFICIENCY

The eleventh edition of the *Encyclopaedia Britannica* states a simple heating principle: "If the flue pipe be carried up a considerable distance inside the apartment to be warmed before being turned into the external air, practically the whole of the heat generated will be utilized." The masonry stove uses this principle in accomplishing heat transfer to the room.

In an earlier wood-burning era, Americans often used yards and yards of stovepipe on their iron stoves. In this way they got the benefit of heat that would otherwise have gone up the chimney. But there were penalties: Creosote dripped on the heads of long-suffering church-goers; pipes thirty feet and more in length were a filthy nuisance to clean; if the creosote caught fire the whole length of stovepipe might collapse and set a building on fire. The long steel stovepipe was and is a dangerous proposition.

Masonry stoves simply take the long-pipe principle and put it inside the stove. Once hot gases leave the firebox, they travel back and forth and up and down through a maze of masonry flues or smoke channels within the stove. The smoke channels may continue for several yards. By the time gases reach the chimney, they have lost most of their heat to the masonry; from the masonry the heat makes its way into the room.

Masonry stoves have cleanouts providing access to these internal passages. A certain amount of fly ash may build up in them over the years, but there should be no soot or creosote if the stove is properly built and operated. Cleaning in central Europe occurs once in five or ten years, I'm told. Gustav Jung, the Viennese stove builder, reported that not long ago he had just checked for the first time the flues in his own stove, built twenty years ago; they were still clean.

EFFICIENCY NUMBERS

Efficiency numbers vary depending on who does the testing and how. Don't think of them in an absolute sense. The numbers are most useful in showing relative performance, comparing one type of heating system with another. The Department of Mechanical Engineering at Auburn University in Alabama did some tests and came up with the efficiency figures for the U.S. Department of Energy which are listed in the box on page 66. They were published in the *Design Handbook for Residential Woodburning Equipment*, Auburn, Alabama, June 1981.

Masonry fireplace	−10% to 10%
Manufactured fireplace	−10% to 10%
Manufactured fireplace with circulation and outside combustion air	10% to 30%
Freestanding fireplace	−10% to 20%
Fireplace/stove	20% to 40%
Radiant stove	50% to 70%
Circulator stoves	40% to 55%
Fireplace inserts	35% to 50%
Furnaces	40% to 60%

Dr. Jay Shelton's tests of wood-burning stoves show basically similar results. The typical stove used by most Americans today is the radiant stove, listed at 50 to 70 percent efficiency. The standard model is a box stove, more or less airtight, and here the Shelton tests showed efficiencies of 50 to 55 percent. Dr. Shelton got efficiencies as high as 65 percent for airtight, radiant iron stoves that had extra heat chambers, through which gases passed after leaving the firebox but before reaching the chimney. His tests showed that the more radiating surface there is, the higher efficiency is likely to be. Very few stoves with extra heat chambers are sold in the U.S., however; typically they are Scandinavian models like the Lange 6303 or 6302K. In practice most Americans use a box stove that offers 50 to 55 percent efficiency.

What about masonry stoves?

So far as I am aware, no tests have been done under laboratory conditions in the U.S., or under any other conditions. In Europe, I sought out efficiency figures in every region where masonry stoves are used. I got figures for Finland, Russia, central Europe, Sweden, and Lithuania. All replies fell in the same range: 70 to 90 percent. It is just the range to be expected from Marcus Bull's tests conducted one hundred fifty years ago. As you add radiating surface, heat-transfer efficiency increases. (NOTE: Calculated by U.S. methods, these European efficiency figures might be a few degrees lower. They would still remain at the high end of the scale, in relative terms, for all wood-burning devices.)

Don't take the foregoing as a blanket indictment of iron stoves, or as blind praise for the masonry models. Europeans feel their masonry stoves are very efficient today. But many early models were not, as the following pages will suggest. Heat transfer can be tricky through massive stove walls. I suspect some of the more crude U.S. models of recent years may in fact have rather low efficiency because of design defects. As for iron stoves, their efficiency does not have to be as low as it commonly is, either. In fact, it could be improved markedly. All that is required are manufacturers willing to make the stoves, and a public willing to buy them. The Lange company's model 6302KG, with two heat chambers above the firebox, offers a good example of what can be done. The new Jøtul 201, with its refractory firebox, appears to offer another example, though I have not had an opportunity to test it myself.

STABILITY

Masonry stoves are stable in the sense that they are massive structures which, once heated, cool slowly. They add to the thermal stability of a building even when the fire is out. If the sun warms a room, the masonry stove and its chimney will absorb solar heat and release it gradually after the sun drops. The stove thus offers a particularly good backup for solar systems by adding to the heat storage capacity of the house. Iron stoves, having little mass in which to store heat, cool quickly after the fire dies. Many of our existing houses were built on something very like the iron stove (or tin box) principle; when the fire goes out, these buildings cool quickly. They possess little heat storage mass.

In some conditions, thermal stability can be a drawback. If you have fired the stove and the weather changes, the stove won't cool for hours. The house may overheat and you will find yourself opening windows. In practice people adapt by keeping a closer eye on the weather and anticipating changes.

Weather change for the masonry stove owner becomes a problem as a rule only in mild periods, during spring and fall. One solution is to have a cookstove or small iron stove for use during these periods, when little heat is needed. If worse comes to worst, opening a window is something less than a calamity. All this suggests why masonry stoves are designed differently according to climate. In milder climates the more responsive stove with thinner walls makes sense. Massive stoves are best for cold regions, where much heat must be stored and overheating is less likely.

Perhaps it has occurred to you to build a small fire during mild weather. Resist the impulse. The small fire does not heat the firebox to the desired level; combustion is incomplete; flues get dirty. What you should do instead is build a fire of shorter duration. Burn hot and fast but for a short time. Then the stove doesn't get as hot but combustion efficiency remains good.

CLAY CONSTRUCTION

The basic building material in all traditional masonry stoves is clay: clay brick, clay tile, clay mortar. The reason is simple: the expansion/contraction factor. Where all stove parts are made of the same kind of clay, they will expand and contract in unison. This is critical in designing and building masonry stoves.

In Europe experienced stove masons will go out of their way to make clay mortar from the same type of clay used to make brick or tile for the stove. The reason is that clays are different. One clay will have more sand in it than the next, or a different kind of sand; the clay will be "thin" or it will be "fat" or "greasy." Different clays have different expansion/contraction factors. Where clay is uniform throughout, there is no conflict as heat causes parts of the stove to expand.

STRESS

The Achilles' heel of the masonry stove is heat stress. When you design a firebox for very high temperatures, when you fill it with fuel and let the fire burn as hot as it will, acute stresses develop. Much of the care that goes into designing and building a stove must be devoted to accommodating this stress. Firebox temperatures may hit 2,000°F. You need durable materials; you must allow for expansion and contraction. Areas taking the heaviest blasts of heat must be able to withstand the stress. Otherwise, cracks appear in the stove; Mother Nature has created an expansion joint where you failed to anticipate the need for one.

There is a school of thought, current among some U.S. masonry stove builders, that stress cracks are to be expected and ignored as harmless. (I've even heard a European say the same thing, but then he had his *own* brand of stoves to sell and of course they did not crack!) Now it is true that small stress cracks are often of no structural importance. It is true also that they can often be patched easily and successfully, and that the stove can continue to work perfectly well. Still, I know a very able American mason who has worked on his masonry stove designs until they do not crack. I know European builders who tell me their stoves do not crack, and I believe them. I have seen photos of very old Tyrolean stoves, made of clay and river stones, that showed no cracks. I've talked to one of the very few people still able to build such stoves, and he assured me that crackless models are quite possible. Needless to say, I'm partial to his approach. My advice is to patch cracks if they appear. But as a designer or builder, don't accept them as inevitable. If you have doubts about your mason's skills where this is concerned, then consider using one of the iron fireboxes described in chapters 10 and 11. The iron firebox sharply reduces stress cracking problems.

FUEL

Masonry heating systems of various designs burn just about any fuel you can imagine: wood, coal, coke, peat, brush, straw, reeds, briquettes. Tile stoves are such a traditional part of life in places like Germany and Switzerland that oil-fired and electric models have appeared in modern times. The traditional wood burning and hay-burning systems were all designed to be fired hot and fast. That is, they were designed for intermittent firing, once or twice a day; short-duration fires were used as needed. This contrasts with continuous combustion firing for a coal- or coke-burning model equipped with a special iron firebox. Today such fireboxes are also often used for wood.

Many Americans tend to look for a wood stove with a big door and a big firebox. Not unreasonably, they want to reduce woodcutting and firetending chores. Big chunks take less cutting, burn longer. But in the household stove they tend to lead to slow fires and poor combustion. Big chunks are not at all well suited to the rapid hot combustion wanted in a masonry stove. Nothing over a three-inch diameter is a common rule of thumb in central Europe. Faggots, bundles of twigs and branches tied tightly together, are an old and very good masonry stove fuel. The smaller wood produces better air/fuel mixing in the firebox, and better combustion.

Some masonry stoves built experimentally in the U.S. in recent years have had very large fireboxes to accommodate four-foot wood. The use of big wood in such fireboxes, or of small fires inadequate to heat the firebox, will lead to creosote. It will also defeat one major virtue of the masonry stove: the possibility for efficient, clean combustion. So firebox design and fuel are also key elements in masonry stove design.

HOW MUCH HEAT?

Traditional masonry stoves were never intended to heat a big house. They were designed to heat a room, perhaps two rooms, but only a part of the house.

A stove—any stove, iron or masonry—is an area heater, not a central heater. In the dwellings where masonry stoves were commonly used, the family clustered around a warm core within the building in winter. Peripheral rooms, if they existed, were allowed to remain cool; or they were heated only occasionally and with separate stoves, like the old four o'clock stove of America, lighted in the afternoon to warm a bedroom for the evening. Fuel was often scarce and it was hard labor to gather it. People could not afford to heat rooms that were not in full-time use. The stove provided heat just where it was required at the moment, and thus it conserved fuel. Today people often expect a stove alone to do the work of a central heating system, and sometimes it will. But usually it is asking too much of the stove, especially in a cold climate.

Some masonry stoves built in America in recent years *can* provide all the heat necessary for an entire house. Fred Fitzpatrick currently uses a model that costs $2,200 installed to heat his 1,800-square-foot house in Groton, Massachusetts. He fires the stove once a day full blast, for about three hours. He burns about six cords of pine each year, which he picks up free at the dump. This man fires his stove very intensely, however, and the

stress on masonry is considerable. It shows in stress cracks. This doesn't bother the owner; the cracks aren't of structural importance, and he can patch them. Besides, the stove is in the basement, where "the aesthetics don't matter." So he is quite happy with his stove, and well he might be. The cost was well below that for a furnace; the house is comfortable, the fuel free for the present, and the stove provides more hot water than his family of four can use. It might sound like a fairy story, but I've seen it work.

So it is indeed possible to heat the entire house with a masonry stove. This is especially true in newer, heavily insulated houses that have open floor plans, which allow good air circulation. Don't count on the same results with an older house; insulation and air circulation may not be good enough. And, unless the stove is designed for it, the stress on the masonry may be so great that cracks appear.

DAMPERS

Dampers are an important consideration in masonry stove design. My advice is: Never use a damper that closes all the way. Beyond that, see the discussions in chapters 9, 11, and 13.

Chapter 6

Heat Beneath the Floor

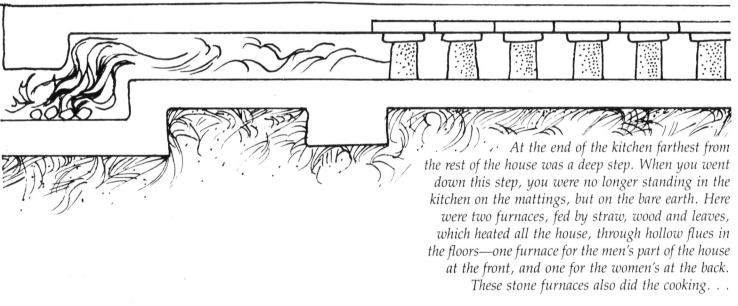

At the end of the kitchen farthest from the rest of the house was a deep step. When you went down this step, you were no longer standing in the kitchen on the mattings, but on the bare earth. Here were two furnaces, fed by straw, wood and leaves, which heated all the house, through hollow flues in the floors—one furnace for the men's part of the house at the front, and one for the women's at the back. These stone furnaces also did the cooking. . .

Younghill Kang*

*The Grass Roof. Charles Scribner's Sons, New York and London, 1966.

Truly efficient European stoves began to appear only in the seventeenth and eighteenth centuries. Long before that, two thousand and perhaps four thousand years ago, certain other societies had quite effective systems for circulating heat beneath the floor. Possibly the oldest of these systems, the *tawakhaneh*, meaning "hot room," can still be found in Afghanistan. A similar system, the *k'ang*, remains in use in China while its close relation, the *ondol*, is the traditional heating system of Korea. The most sophisticated of all the subfloor systems, the hypocaust, appeared more than two thousand years ago in Rome.

Ancient subfloor systems all operate on the heat-storage principle: fire warms masonry, masonry warms the room. In this instance the space beneath the floor constitutes a plenum through which warm air moves by natural draft. The floor itself is made of masonry, and as the floor warms it heats the room above. Sometimes flues are arranged to warm the walls as well.

Subfloor heating systems, particularly the Roman hypocaust, are often described as an ancient form of central heating. But that is not really the case. They are seldom built to heat more than one or two rooms. The natural draft within the system is sufficient to move warm air about beneath a room or two. It is not sufficient to move air to more distant points in a building. For that the pumps and blowers of modern central heating are necessary.

The idea behind the ancient systems is sound. They can be very comfortable to live with. Some would say they are the most comfortable *heating* systems of all and this is perhaps why, in one form or another, they remain in use. The old systems did have drawbacks. They had to be very carefully built and maintained; otherwise they could be not only troublesome but dangerous. For the most part they must have been inefficient, but today's techniques make it possible to construct subfloor systems that are both efficient and safe. That makes the old systems worth a closer look, since the principle is little used today in North America.

TAWAKHANEH

In the summer of 1977 I received a letter from Dr. Louis Dupree, an American anthropologist and expert on Afghanistan. He had just inspected a Russian team's excavation in Afghan Turkestan, and he believed it contained the remains of an ancient tawakhaneh. The site was Bronze Age, dating from about 2,000 B.C. If Dr. Dupree's finding proves correct, that would make the tawakhaneh the oldest floor-heating system known by about two thousand years. It would also raise the possibility that such systems spread from that part of the world to both the East and West along ancient trade routes. It would not be the first such occurrence. The windmill may also have originated in Khorasan on the Iranian/Afghan frontier, spreading from there to both China and Europe. In this respect it may be significant (and I have my friend Patrick A. O'Sullivan to thank for this information) that the name for this Afghan heating system is borrowed from Persian.

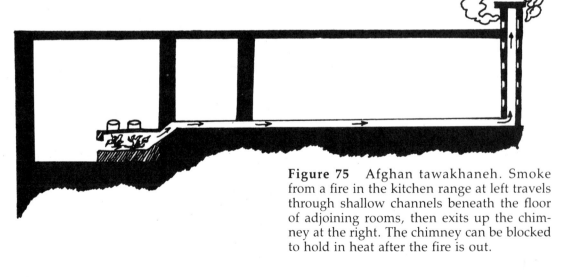

Figure 75 Afghan tawakhaneh. Smoke from a fire in the kitchen range at left travels through shallow channels beneath the floor of adjoining rooms, then exits up the chimney at the right. The chimney can be blocked to hold in heat after the fire is out.

The most detailed account of the tawakhaneh that I have seen is by H.-J. Wald, and the following information is based on it. Wald described a system used to heat a teahouse in the Logar Valley, a high mountain region south of Kabul where winters are harsh and long. The source of heat was a kitchen range two meters long and one meter wide, built of fired clay tile. Pots were set into holes in the stovetop; fuel was wood or dung. Hot gases from the firebox passed out of the range into four parallel ducts. These ran beneath the floor of two adjoining rooms, then channeled the smoke into a chimney on the end wall of the farther room. The first room was small, about sixty-five square feet, and because it was warmest served as a bath; the second room was about ten by twenty-three feet. It served for sleeping and dining. Wald said he had heard of, but not seen, a tawakhaneh that heated a second-floor level as well as the ground floor.

The ducts were each about twenty-nine inches wide and five inches high. They were walled with tile and roofed over with slabs of slate an inch and a half thick. The slate in turn was covered by a layer of clay, packed hard in an effort to prevent gas leaks through the floor. The chimney had a cap on its top, and smoke emerged through an opening just below this cap. Once the fire in the range had been reduced to coals and there was no more smoke, these chimney openings could be closed and heat

Figure 76 Chinese k'ang. The raised-brick platform is warmed in this instance by hot gases from a fire in the cooking stove at right. The stove has a wok set into its top. The brick platform is used for sleeping at night, but by day it may be used for a variety of purposes. In this scene, reconstructed from old photographs, a game is in progress.

held in the system. However, the clay floor would tend to shrink and crack with heat and time; combustion fumes would then leak into the room, especially after chimney vents were closed. The floor required constant vigilance to prevent leaks and herein lies the weakness of the system, evidenced by headache complaints among Afghans who use it. The *tanur*, a kind of oven, is also sometimes used as a heat source for the tawakhaneh.

ONDOL AND K'ANG

Both the Korean ondol and the Chinese k'ang often (but not always) use the warmth of cooking fires to warm floors. Sometimes smoke is carried beneath the floor through parallel ducts, as in Afghanistan; sometimes the masonry floor is supported on a forest of pillars or piers, among which hot gases circulate.

In north and northwest China the typical k'ang of recent times is actually a sleeping platform, a kind of raised mud-brick bed extending along one wall of a room. The platform is wide enough and long enough for the whole family to sleep on. It may be fired through its own furnace or stokehole, or it may be warmed by a kitchen range, often located in the adjoining room as with the tawakhaneh. Family members may sit on the k'ang during the day to do household chores. At night the quilts come out and the k'ang becomes a bed. Dr. Joseph Needham, Cambridge University's distinguished student of Chinese civilization, found the k'ang a hard bed to sleep on but "very comfortable in icy weather."

One drawback Dr. Needham did note: a tendency for the straw used in making mud bricks to catch fire and set the whole bed smoldering during the night, no doubt a memorable experience. The mud bricks may become heavily laden with soot by springtime, and in rural areas they are sometimes pulverized and spread on the garden as fertilizer. The k'ang is then rebuilt.

The k'ang was common in Han times two thousand years ago, and thus is probably of even earlier origin. In the past it assumed forms other than the sleeping platform, and these were described by Jean-Joseph de Grammont (1736–1812), a Jesuit mathematician and astronomer who lived for many years in China. Grammont defined three types of k'ang. One was the *kao-k'ang*, the sleeping platform just described. The second was the *ti-k'ang*, a floor-warming system. The third was the *tong-k'ang*, which warmed a masonry wall.

The sleeping platform and the floor-heating system as described by Grammont were built alike. In both the floor was supported on pillars. The pillars were spaced to support tiles up to two

feet square that formed the base of the floor. The brick furnace had a vaulted roof and extended channel to carry heat well under the floor. The remarkable thing about this is the close resemblance in construction detail to the Roman hypocaust. The chief difference lay in smoke outlets; the hypocaust had many, the k'ang but one or two. Appearances suggest a common origin. But appearances can deceive, and there doesn't seem to be direct evidence.

Fuel has long been precious in China, as in so many lands inhabited by man in large numbers. Every available scrap tends to be put to use. A missionary, Arthur H. Smith, described the scene at the turn of the century when "The vast army of fuel gatherers . . . overspread all the land." Scarcely a leaf escaped their bamboo rakes; boys climbed trees with clubs and beat the limbs to make leaves fall. Even straws, said Smith, "are scarcely allowed leisure to show which way the wind blows."

Straw, leaves, wood, pine cones and needles, dried plant stalks from the fields, all went into the firebox of the k'ang and ondol. Among the poor, to whom fuel was most precious, the k'ang was built so that smoke exited into the room housing it. People of middle income channeled smoke into an adjoining room. The well-to-do channeled smoke outdoors through a hole in the wall or a chimney. The explanation seems clear: The poor had to use every bit of heat and so retained the smoke for what warmth it could offer. The well-off could

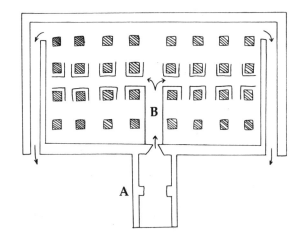

Figure 77 This illustration shows the kao-k'ang (or heated sleeping platform) from above, as it appeared to the French Jesuit, Father Grammont, in eighteenth-century China. In the illustration, A represents the firebox, built of brick with an arched or vaulted roof; B is the furnace extension or tongue that carries gases from the firebox toward the center of the heating chamber or plenum beneath the floor. The pillars supporting the floor above this chamber are twelve to eighteen inches high. They rest on a floor of clay, paving tiles, or brick. The pillars support tiles up to two feet square and four inches thick, which form the base for the floor. Smoke makes its way out of the k'ang through (in this case) two openings at opposite ends. Grammont said the floor k'ang, like the ondol, had only one smoke outlet. This arrangement of smoke outlets suggests heat distribution trouble, with hot spots along the most direct path between furnace tongue and smoke outlet. Grammont had little to say of the tong-k'ang or wall heater except that "the heating flue is carried along the floor, with openings from it at which the smoke ascends into the spaces of a hollow wall." The wall contains horizontal smoke passages, the end of each letting into the passage above.

afford some heat loss in the interest of a smoke-free house.

Frugality with fuel is ingrained in Chinese life. In the West we've taken up the wok, a traditional Chinese cooking vessel, without really considering what its design implies: fuel shortage. The wok is made of thin metal that transmits heat quickly from the fire. Wok recipes call for food cut into small pieces; these cook rapidly. The small pieces are spread over a broad surface in the wok so that, again, heat hasn't far to penetrate. The flash fire from a few handfuls of straw or pine needles becomes enough to cook a meal. The western roast, requiring hours to cook, is food for a fuel-rich society.

Frugality with fuel, not to mention windows covered with cloth or paper, led in China to dwellings cold by our standards. At the turn of the century Arthur Smith remarked on this: "The houses are so uncomfortable that even at home if the weather is cold the inmates often wear all the clothes they can put on. When abroad they have no more to add. 'Are you cold?' we often ask. 'Of course' is the constant reply." Australians speak of a three-dog night; Chinese may speak of a four- or five-coat day. Grammont found that in the emperor's apartments at Peking, the temperature with the floor system operating might be 41° to 44°F. But, said Grammont, "the warmth is very gentle and penetrating." In the West today we are a softer people.

At large gatherings, being near the k'ang used to be a question of rank. The principal parties sat on it. Others sat near or far according to status. If the outermost guests were chilly, it was incumbent on the prosperous host to provide fur-lined robes to warm them. Said Grammont, the host "stores his wardrobe against the cold weather, as an Englishman does his cellar with wood and coals."

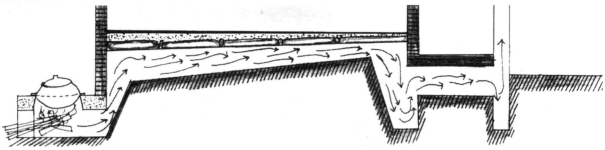

Figures 78 and 79 In the traditional Korean ondol, fire often burns under a round cooking pot in the kitchen area. The smoke then passes upward into heating channels that carry it under the floor of an adjoining room, as shown in figure 78. The channels are formed by laying slabs of granite or slate across ridges made of earth or clay. Typical channel width is about two feet, while the height is only three to four inches. The channel floor is earth, and considerable heat must be lost into the ground as well as along the periphery of the system. Apparently, soot clogging of the channels has also been a problem, to the extent that channels must be torn apart and rebuilt at intervals. The stone floor above the channels is covered by a layer of clay or earth mixed with straw. This in turn is covered by a layer of paper, glued down, and finally by a layer of special heavy oiled paper called *changpan*. The idea of this construction is to keep the floor free of gas leaks. Uneven heat distribution is a problem, as smoke tends to take the most direct path to the single chimney flue outlet. The Koreans try to circumvent this in two ways. They make the floor thicker where heat first strikes it from the fire under the cooking pot. And while it is not indicated in figure 79, which shows one type of ondol from above, the builders also vary the width of openings into the smoke channels. Smoke channel entrances nearest to the fire would be narrowest, and those farthest from the fire the widest, to even out gas flow in the channels. At the point where the smoke channels end as they approach the chimney, a trench or pit is dug at right angles to the channels. (See figure 78.) This is called the *gaijari*, and it creates an eddy effect as smoke enters it, slowing gas movement through the system and thus retaining heat longer beneath the floor. The *gulttukgaijari*, a pit at the chimney base, may play a similar role.

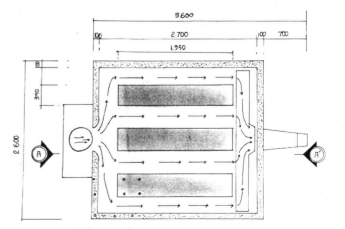

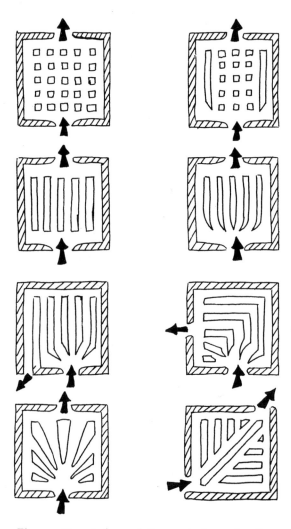

Figure 80 A few of the varied smoke-flow patterns from the Korean ondol, for both channeled and pillared systems.

As in China, so also in Korea. Destruction of forest became so great over the centuries that it led in modern times to the outlawing of wood fuel for the ondol. The modern substitute fuel has been coal, and because of the lethal gases produced it has not been a good substitute. If the ondol floor is poorly built or maintained so that cracks develop, carbon monoxide can leak into the living quarters; fatal results are far from unknown in modern Korea. Centuries ago coal came into use in some areas of China for firing the k'ang, apparently with similarly unhappy results. Both the k'ang and ondol are by nature low-draft systems; gases move through them slowly and leak with ease out of any cracks. With wood fuel this seems to have caused few problems; with coal the difficulties may be acute.

HYPOCAUST

The climate of Rome is mild and offers little incentive for intricate heating systems. Braziers and open fires took the chill off in ancient times. How and why, then, did Rome develop the most complex of ancient heating systems?

Tradition lays the invention of the hypocaust to one Sergius Orata, a wealthy and pleasure-loving businessman from Campania. Around 80 B.C., the ancient writers agree, Orata began using the hypocaust to heat ponds and aquaria where he hatched and raised fish, perhaps even oysters, on a commercial basis. He seems also to have been a shrewd real estate speculator and lover of luxury, a kind of ancient wheeler-dealer.

Now it never seemed reasonable to me that a man like Sergius Orata could have invented such an interesting device as the hypocaust. Exploited it, yes—to raise fish, to make more attractive the country estates that he bought and sold. But invented it? No. Not the type. So it came as a relief to learn that the hypocaust is older than Sergius Orata. Twentieth-century excavations make it clear, according to the British scholar Tony Rook, that hypocausts were in use by the second and perhaps the third centuries B.C., before Orata was born. The possibility remains open that the idea reached Rome from the East. The name hypocaust comes from the Greek meaning "fire beneath." Alexander the Great (356–323 B.C.) and his army visited what is now Afghanistan, even established Greek colonies in the region. Could Alexander's soldiers have brought the idea back with them?

The origins of the hypocaust may never be entirely known. Whatever happened, the consequences of its arrival in Rome were considerable. Romans had a passion for baths and the hypocaust came into wide use for heating them, not only in Rome but throughout the Empire. Initially the hypocaust seems to have been used by the Romans only for bath heating. But as the Empire expanded northward, there came a need for warm living quarters and hypocausts supplied the heat. New forms developed especially for that purpose, and these came into use in Rome as well as in the northern reaches of the Empire. In China and Korea the k'ang and ondol were in use among rich and poor alike, but only the well-to-do among Romans used the hypocaust. The common people could afford nothing better than the brazier and the open fire. For bathing, of course, the public baths were available.

Romans probably spent a greater part of the national income on bathing than any other people in history. The scale seems staggering even today. The bath complex completed by Caracalla in 206 A.D. occupied twenty-seven acres. It could accommodate sixteen hundred bathers in a building seven hundred fifty by five hundred feet. Such baths were really centers of social life; they might contain gymnasia, lecture halls, quiet courtyards for rest and conversation, libraries, sitting rooms, shops, and game areas.

Latter-day cousins of the Roman baths exist today in the *hamams* of North Africa and the Middle East—"Turkish baths" to most Americans. The old Roman four-room pattern often continues: a dressing room or *apodyteria;* the hot bathing room or *caldarium;* the lukewarm bathing room or *tepidarium;* and the cold water plunge or *frigidarium.* The Roman bath might also have had a hot, dry room where one would simply sit and sweat, as in a sauna.

The heat for the bath came from a hypocaust; typically this heated one room, perhaps two or even three but rarely if ever a whole building. Heat moved beneath the floor as in Asian systems, but the Roman system was more complex and better built. And where Asian designs had one or at most two smoke outlets, the Romans had at least half a dozen and often more. These small chimney flues were spaced evenly about the heated room. They contributed their own share of warmth to the room, and theoretically at least they made it possible to distribute heat more evenly under the floor.

In cross-section the flues were sometimes not much larger than a three-by-five card, tiny compared to the chimney flues we use today. The Roman chimneys were low, too, letting smoke out below the eaves instead of above the roof. A consequence of this flue system was very low draft pressure. The taller the chimney and the greater its cross-section, the greater the potential draft. What follows is simple enough: A strong draft rapidly carries not only smoke but much heat up the flue; low draft slows the process and saves heat. Smoke remains longer in the low-draft system, giving up heat all the while.

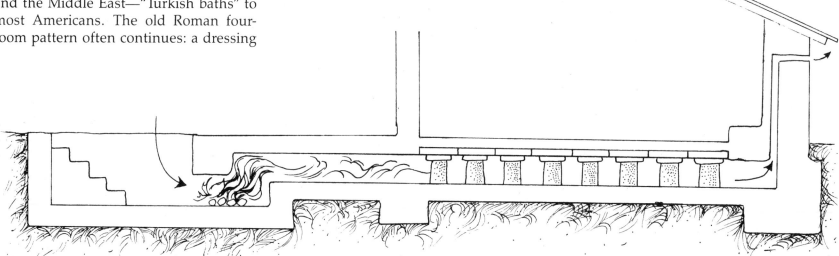

Figure 81 Pillared hypocaust, typically used to heat the baths of ancient Rome.

Figure 82 Remains of a pillared hypocaust in a Roman villa at Chedworth in England. At rear, beyond the tile floor mosaic, are the hollow flue tiles that carried smoke up through the wall of this bathing room.

Draft in the hypocaust was in fact so slight that we have nothing comparable in today's wood-burning systems. In the 1950s Fritz Kretzschmer tested a rebuilt Roman hypocaust at the Saalburg Museum in Bad Homburg, West Germany. He tried to measure draft with an instrument that could be read to one-tenth of a millimeter. The reading was so low it never registered on the instrument. Kretzschmer concluded draft never exceeded one-tenth of a millimeter. In contrast Jay Shelton recently estimated maximum domestic chimney drafts in the U.S. at one-tenth of an *inch* of water pressure. That would be 254 times greater than the supposed maximum draft at the Saalburg. The hypocaust was truly a device of a different order.

Kretzschmer also found the hypocaust very clean. "The minimal gas speed and immeasurably slight draft carries little soot into the heating system. With our instruments we could detect no buildup or precipitates. The chimney sweep's handiwork was superfluous in ancient times. That explains why cleaning openings are rare in hypocaust systems." It is true that Kretzschmer used charcoal, a comparatively clean fuel. The Romans ordinarily fired with wood, which has much greater soot-creating potential. Still the low draft, plus such archaeological evidence as exists, suggest Kretzschmer is right; the hypocaust was a clean system, at least potentially. Problems of soot buildup in Asian systems, like the k'ang and ondol, can be attributed in part to design differences; they might also be caused by different use patterns.

Channeled and pillared hypocausts were the two common types. The pillared system, where heat circulated among a forest of pilings under the floor, transmitted more heat and was common in baths. It may at times have produced too much heat; Seneca complained of baths hot enough "to boil a criminal slave." Doubtless at times the furnace attendant's attention wandered from the fire.

Roman Bath Design

The hanging floors of the hot bath rooms are to be constructed as follows: First, the surface of the ground shall be laid with tiles a foot and a half square, sloping toward the furnace in such a way that, if a ball is thrown in, it cannot stop inside but must return of itself to the furnace room; thus the heat of the fire will more readily spread under the hanging floor. Upon them, pillars made of eight-inch brick are built, and set at such a distance apart that two-foot square tiles may be used to cover them. These pillars should be two feet in height, laid with clay mixed with hair, and covered on top with the two-foot tiles which support the floor.

Vitruvius, first century B.C.

Channeled systems were simpler and less expensive to build; the area below the floor was filled in with masonry, except for trenches cut through to make heat channels. The reduced radiating surface (only the area above the trench) produced less heat. The lower cost and reduced likelihood of overheating made these systems suitable for dwellings,

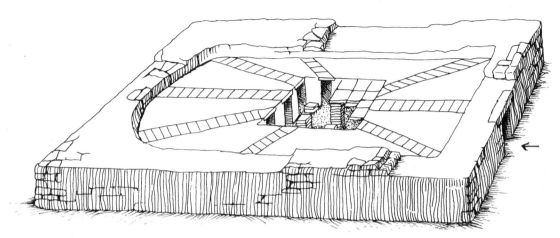

Figure 83 Channeled hypocaust. Smoke from the furnace (arrow at right) traveled to a central pillared section, then dispersed into seven other channels. At the end of each channel was a flue that carried smoke up through the wall. Hypocausts of this type were used to warm parts of a dwelling.

where they are often found. Dr. Dietwulf Baatz, who experimented with a channeled hypocaust at the Saalburg in 1976, found that it heated more slowly than the pillared variety. From a cold start it took four days to bring the masonry up to a comfortable equilibrium temperature. But heat storage capacity was of course greater than in a pillared system. Once the initial warming period was over, it proved possible to keep the room above the channeled system comfortable on one firing of wood a day. The outdoor temperature at the time was around 32°F.

Dr. Baatz found a tendency for the hot gases leaving the furnace to move directly to the nearest flue outlet. This made for uneven heating of the floor. Partial blocking of the flues nearest the furnace corrected this. It seems likely that the

Romans used some sort of damper within each smoke flue to adjust gas flow and thus control heat distribution, but we have no proof.

A third and little-known type of hypocaust warmed rooms primarily through heat circulated in hollow wall tiles. An example turned up in the Roman ruin of Lauriacum at Enns, Austria. The furnace heat passed through a single channel under the floor to the base of a wall, then circulated upward through the tiles. Horizontal as well as vertical passages interconnected the tiles, so warmth penetrated the entire wall.

The building at Lauriacum was not a bath where the use of wall tiles was common, but its true use remains unclear. Fritz Kretzschmer believed the key to the design of this system lay in the reduced

heat storage offered by the relatively thin wall tiles. Channeled and pillared hypocausts respond very slowly; once hot they remain hot, once cooled they are slow to warm. This is fine when weather is stable but it creates problems when there is a sudden change in heating requirements. There is no way to make the system respond rapidly to changed weather, except by opening a window if it is too hot. The wall tiles would have cooled or warmed comparatively quickly. They possessed much less mass and this made the whole system much more responsive to immediate heating needs. The Lauriacum hypocaust lost some of the thermal stability of a pillared or channeled system, but it gained flexibility.

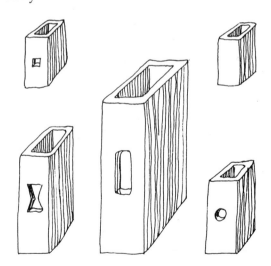

Figure 84 Roman flue tiles. The holes in the sides permitted lateral as well as vertical movement of warmth in the hollow wall of a bath.

The basic hypocaust fuel was wood. Some furnaces in the great baths were enormous and whole tree trunks burned in them. The normal furnace, however, was only somewhat larger than our typical household wood-burning furnace today. Other hypocaust fuels included brush, peat, charcoal, and perhaps occasionally coal. Straw was used in treeless regions, and Pierre Deffontaines described a hypocaustlike system fired by straw in rural Spain. It seems likely this derived from a Roman model.

Hypocaust Features

The following outline of hypocaust features may help in understanding the design of these systems.

Heat chamber or **plenum** In bath construction the heat chamber was entirely open and the floor above it supported on pillars; in the channeled hypocaust heat circulated primarily through channels cut into the masonry below the floor.

Furnace Furnaces were usually rectangular, sometimes circular, and had vaulted roofs. Size varied according to heating needs. A typical furnace found in Germany was set two feet, eight inches into the ground and steps led down to it for firing. The firebox was four feet eight by four feet, four inches, and the stokehole eight by fourteen inches, or close to the size of a contemporary woodstove door. The construction was masonry with stone, tile or firebrick lining the firebox. There was no grate.

Furnace extension or **tongue** Many but not all hypocausts had this feature. The tongue was a channel that led hot gases from the furnace into the heat chamber or plenum of a pillared hypocaust. Floor and walls of the tongue were made of brick; the distance between these walls was one-third to one-fifth the furnace width. Where a furnace served more than one room, two tongues might lead off in different directions; it seems clear they were intended to improve heat distribution.

Pillars Floor supports for the pillared hypocaust were commonly six to eight inches square and built of tile, brick, cement, or stone. Height was normally sixteen to twenty-four inches but occasionally up to forty-eight inches.

Floor Typically this was about eight inches thick. The base was a platform of twenty-four-inch-square tiles resting on the pillars. Above this was a thin layer of cement or clay. Above this a thick course of cement mixed with gravel. Above this was the finish floor of the room above, in the baths often a tile mosaic or a layer of marble. Layering the floor tended to frustrate cracking and penetration of gases from the heat chamber below. Floor thickness also helped here, as well as the high quality of Roman cement.

Chimney flues The hypocaust had at least four to six chimneys, often more. These were small flues located in a pillared hypocaust at the four corners of the room and toward the center of the walls. In a channeled hypocaust there would be one flue at the end of each channel. The flues let smoke out below the eaves, at times only ten to fourteen feet above ground. And they were located on the inner wall of the room, never the outer, so that whatever heat they might transmit could be used. Frequently three sides of the flue protruded into the room to provide extra heat-radiating surface.

Tubuli The term refers to Roman tiles that were used specifically for heating wall surface. Ordinary chimney tiles were much like our chimney tiles today, simple boxlike structures. But the tubuli had slots in their sides and permitted sideways movement of heat within the walls. The tubuli were sometimes used in baths for extra heat, in combination with a pillared hypocaust. At Enns rooms in a Roman building were heated entirely by such a wall-tile system.

EFFICIENCY AND SAFETY IN SUB-FLOOR SYSTEMS

Calculating efficiency in the ancient systems is difficult because the systems themselves vary so much from one to the next. One hypocaust may use a fully open plenum to warm the floor; another hypocaust may use only channels; a third hypocaust may use an open plenum and four walls lined with hollow tiles, all radiating warmth into the room. The possibilities for variation are obviously great.

After looking at the variables, Tony Rook concluded: "Such a system defies theoretical analysis." Still he made the effort, for a Roman bath he had himself excavated at Welwyn in Herfordshire. There Rook estimated efficiency at 41.5

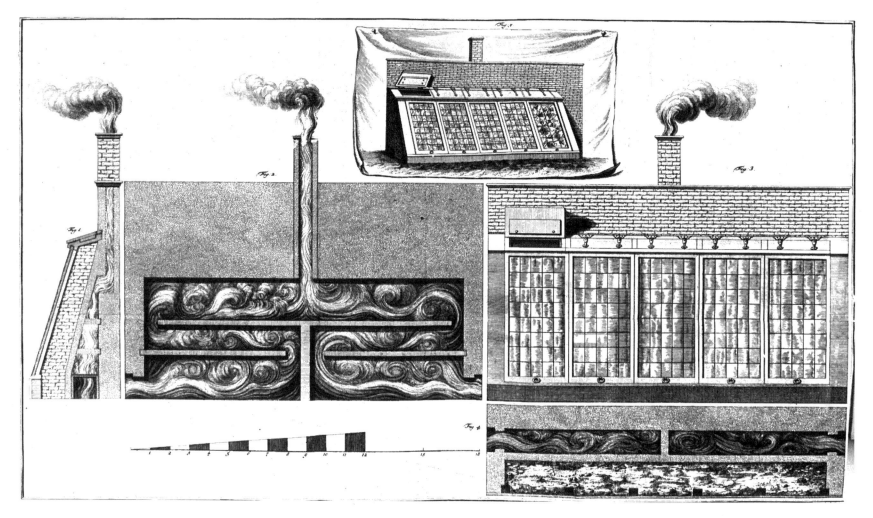

Figure 85 During the eighteenth century, floor and wall flues became a common means of heating greenhouses in England and on the Continent. The Dutch forcing frame above relies on such flues for heat. From the Leyden University Library Collection.

percent. Closing things up so that only the necessary air for combustion moved through the system might, Rook felt, push efficiency to 50 percent but no higher. (Whether the Romans did this is not presently known.)

Heribert Hüser, who in the 1970s fired the same Saalburg hypocaust used by Kretzschmer, felt Rook's 41.5 percent figure was "realistic, but only if the hypocaust was fired with considerable surplus air."

Hüser makes a particularly interesting point. In his own tests, creosote formed in the wall flues and permeated the wall. But, he said, evidence of wall paintings and mosaics in Roman buildings leads to the conclusion that the Romans had solved the problem of condensation. That is, there is no sign of creosote forming in the wall flues or staining the wall paintings. Kretzschmer makes a similar observation: Hypocausts seem to have burned cleanly. Yet the ancient literature carries accounts of billowing smoke as slaves fired the Roman baths, and billowing smoke is the sign of poor combustion. The scholars, then, have more work to do before we come to a full understanding of how well these systems worked. Meanwhile, I think some seat-of-the-pants conclusions are possible, as follows.

Most ancient subfloor systems were not efficient by modern standards. Smoke passages of the ondol were shallow, just a few inches deep; soot clogged them so that the floor had to be torn up to clean them. This indicates poor combustion. The shallow depth meant hot gases were as much in contact with the ground as with the floor above. Thus heat went into the ground, and around the periphery of the system this must have meant considerable heat loss. The Romans deepened the plenum so that the hot gases stratified: the hottest near the floor, the cooler gases down near the ground. This was an improvement. Still there must have been large heat loss around the edges of the plenum.

So, low combustion efficiency was frequent if not universal, and heat transfer efficiency suffered because of losses from the plenum. The most efficient systems were those combining floor heat with wall heat. Kretzschmer estimated the efficiency of one such (in Trier) at 90 percent, but this seems far too high. Hüser has suggested that our ordinary methods of calculating efficiency just do not seem to apply to the hypocaust, and Rook seems to agree. It wouldn't surprise me if both were correct. The hypocaust's low draft is unlike anything else in the heating world. Hüser also felt that the hypocaust might prove a reasonable means of heating in the modern era, and I would agree. The major failings of the old subfloor systems can be eliminated today, first by designing the firebox for good combustion, and second by insulating the plenum against heat loss.

As to safety, the ancient systems had one obvious drawback, gas leakage from the plenum into the living space. This was particularly troublesome in Korea and Afghanistan, probably also in China. The Roman systems with their thicker and better-constructed floors were perhaps safer, but the risk remained. Here again there is a modern solution: Use the furnace to heat air or water and channel that beneath the floor to warm it, instead of the flue gases. The risk then disappears.

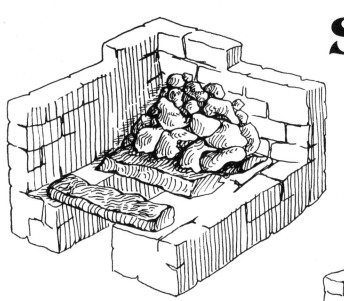

Chapter 7

Stone Ovens and Smoke Eaters

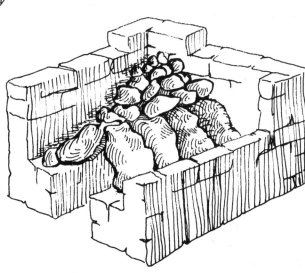

Perhaps a thousand years ago, sometime between the ninth and twelfth centuries, there appeared in Europe a device that would be familiar to modern solar architects. This was the *steinofen*, or stone oven, which stored heat in a pile of rocks. The rock pile was set below the living floor of the building that it warmed, as with many solar storage beds today.

THE STONE OVEN

There is a theory that the steinofen descends from the Roman hypocaust. It may be so. There is surely a question here worth asking: Why, if the hypocaust was such a good heating device, did it not remain in use in the colder parts of the empire? As the Roman presence melted away in the north, did their technology decline as well?

I suspect the answer is that much technology did decline. Still it would be surprising if the hypocaust did not, here and there, get some use after the Romans departed. This is speculation; the evidence is thin. Prof. Pierre Riché writes of Pepin the Short restoring the old Roman baths at Aix in the eighth century. Whether a hypocaust was part of them he does not say; it would be surprising if it were not. Then there is the celebrated plan drawn up in 820 for the Abbey of St. Gall in what is now Switzerland. The plan includes a heating system often described as a hypocaust. Others believe it may be a transitional form between hypocaust and stone oven.

Figure 86 Stone oven from Germany, 1666. Courtesy Deutsches Museum.

The stone oven did in some ways resemble the hypocaust. Both systems channeled outside air into the heating system. Both supplied heat from below. The stone oven was often fired from outside the building; often also it used a wall flue to carry off smoke, again, like the hypocaust. Both systems were beyond the budgets of ordinary folk. The steinofen appeared in castles, fortresses, and the private dwellings of the well-to-do. It was also used in those cloisters that did not altogether forbid the use of heat.

These kindred features aside, there is at least an equally striking resemblance between stone ovens and the traditional kilns, drying ovens, and rock pile stoves of north Europe. Heating a stone pile was a widespread and very ancient practice in north Europe. This simple tech-

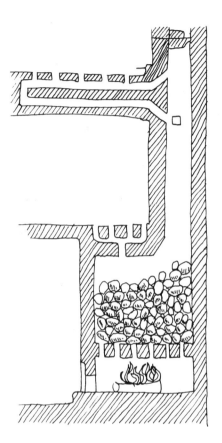

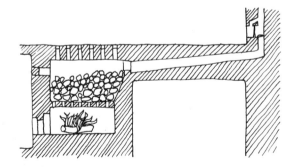

Figures 87 and 88 Massive stone ovens of a type found in castles and public buildings. These seem to have had a prodigious heating capacity.

nology may have contributed as much to the origins of the stone oven as did the hypocaust.

The stone oven consisted of a fire chamber with a plate on top. Upon this plate stood a pile of granite or basalt rocks, or sometimes a heap of iron balls. The rock pile itself was enclosed within a masonry vault. From the vault led wooden ducts that had been lined with clay to make them fireproof. (The clay had been laced with horsehair, in an effort to prevent its cracking away from the wood.) One duct led the smoke out via a wall flue. One or more other ducts channeled warm air to the rooms above, the air entering through holes cut into the floor. As the system was fired, heat and flame thrust up into the rock pile through holes in the plate covering the firebox.

Stone ovens were often large. Hermann Vetter described one at Marienburg with a firebox more than ten feet on a side and three and a half feet high. Resting above this were four hundred to five hundred cubic feet of fieldstone. The idea was to fire the system with wood for several hours, until the stones reached red heat. During firing the chimney duct was open but the holes admitting warmth to rooms were closed by a heavy plate drawn over them. When the stones reached red heat the fire was allowed to die and the chimney closed by a damper. Then the floor vents were opened. In the old city hall in Luneburg the seats of city councillors were arranged so that they sat just above the floor vents.

Figure 89 Stone oven of a type found in some larger private homes.

It took a great deal of wood to fire a big stone oven. Heat loss up the flue during firing would have been substantial. Still their performance, as recorded in 1822 by an architect named Voss, is impressive. Voss tested the stone furnace at Marienburg whose dimensions are given above. After firing for three and a half hours, all remaining coals were removed from the firebox and the chimney damper shut. Vents were then opened into the refectory above, and air entered the room at 200°C (392°F). Within twenty minutes the room temperature rose from 6° to 23°C (43° to 73.4°F). The following day without further firing the vents were again opened and air entered the room at 148°C (298.4°F). Four days later the air came in at 75°C (167°F) and eight days later at 46°C (114.8.F). On each occasion

the air was warm enough to heat the room.

There is more one could wish to know about Voss's experiment. He seems to have consumed a great quantity of wood in the short firing period. This was softwood, probably in the form of bundles of faggots rather than large logs. Voss complained that the fieldstones he

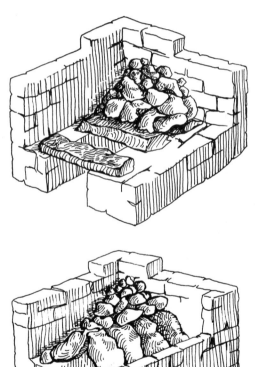

Figure 90 Stone stacking technique, as used in typical east Baltic stone ovens used for the sauna or as drying kilns.

used to store heat tended to disintegrate at high temperatures, blocking the holes through which the heat and flame rose to warm them. No doubt granite or basalt rock, or iron balls, would have fared better. But with modifications to make firing efficient, to improve safety, and to prevent heat loss, it is not difficult to imagine a stone oven operating efficiently today.

OTHER SUBFLOOR SYSTEMS

From time to time in the literature of heating, one comes on old and sometimes puzzling references to floor-warming in England, continental Europe, even in America. Abroad, much of this appears to have been confined to hothouses, and it has been well described by John Hix in his book, *The Glass House.* The cultivation of tropical plants as well as medicinal herbs grew popular among the well-to-do during the seventeenth and eighteenth centuries. The plants required warmth to get them through the winter, and an early means of providing this was through smoke flues built beneath the floor of the greenhouses. These subfloor systems were crude and inefficient. Some may have been influenced by Chinese designs, as these were (perhaps imperfectly) understood through descriptions published at the time.

Some of the greenhouses warmed by wood were enormous. The Imperial Botanic Garden at St. Petersburg contained a complex of glass houses almost three quarters of a mile long with buildings that rose above thirty feet. Log fires built at twelve-hour intervals kept the czar's botanical collections healthy through the winter, though wood consumption must have been prodigious. In the nineteenth century the smoke flue heating systems were generally replaced by steam.

Another English system that resulted in a degree of floor-warming derives from a stove developed by the French physicist André Dalesme in 1680. Dalesme's stove caused people to marvel when it was first demonstrated. The fire was open, right out in the room. Yet there was no smoke. Dalesme achieved this by establishing a strong chimney draft, strong enough to draw smoke downward through the base of the stove and then horizontally until it reached the chimney. Benjamin Franklin first saw such stoves in England, and later devised one himself, though it was never produced commercially. In a letter to Samuel Cooper in 1773, Franklin described two such stoves that he had seen that year in the Bank of England and at Lincoln's Hall Inn. The stoves, he said, "are placed in the middle of the respective rooms. The smoke of these descends, and passing underground, rises in some chimney at a distance." The method eliminated unsightly stovepipes. The main warming effect came from the iron portion of the stove exposed in the middle of the room, rather than from the flue beneath the floor.

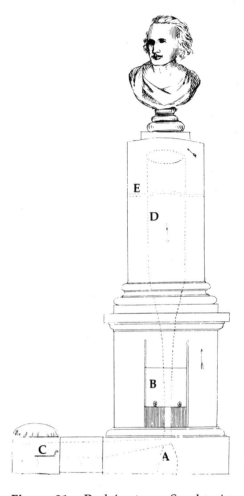

Figure 91 Peale's stove. Smoke rises from the firebox (B) into the pedestal (E), descends through the perforated tube (D), which again carries smoke through the firebox, where it is consumed. Gases then descend into the passage (A), which carries them under the floor to a chimney flue. Above the point marked C was a viewing hole, so that visitors could gaze down into the passage beneath the floor and see that there was no "smoke" leaving Peale's smoke eater.

Charles Wilson Peale of Philadelphia also designed such stoves, which he called "smoke eaters." He built them in Philosophical Hall and in the State House. According to Prof. Samuel Y. Edgerton, Jr., Peale described the stoves "as being of brick, bound with iron hoops [to keep the heated brick from cracking], plastered and painted in imitation of marble, and surmounted by a square pedestal of classic design with a bust on top. As the smoke rose inside the pedestal it was sucked down into perforated pipes extending through the fire. The smoke would be consumed as it became exposed to the heat through these perforations and the hot air itself would continue in the ducts which led down the stove and out under the floor itself to the chimney! Peale would open a vent in the floor to show his amazed visitors the passage of clear, warm and smokeless air." But Peale's brick stove remained, like Franklin's iron model, a curiosity.

Another American subfloor heating system was built into the House of Representatives in 1808. This involved the installation of several stoves on the floor below the House Chamber. There in a cavity three to five feet deep beneath the members' seats ran some two hundred feet of flue carrying smoke from the stoves en route to the chimney. Benjamin L. Walbert III, an architect who looked into this system, felt it might have been "a variation on the Roman hypocaust." The architect who devised it, Benjamin Latrobe, had studied in England and was no doubt aware of subfloor heating systems there. Whatever its origins, the House system seems to have flopped; Latrobe said he had wanted to use steam all along, anyway.

Chapter 8

East European Stoves

These [dwellings], whether subterranean or not, are usually oblong, and divided into three apartments, the middle one of which opens into the two others. From the central compartment a large clay furnace, or rather an immense oven, usually whitewashed on the outside, projects into the room occupied by the family, and furnishes an agreeable warmth. For a floor, the inmates use a piece of the soil which God gave to be lived upon, while a raised divan or a simple bank of earth around three sides of the room, is so covered with mats and blankets as to serve as seats by day and a couch by night.

James O. Noyes, M.D.*

*From *Roumania*, New York, 1857.

krainian hunters sat out the last glacial period in huts made of hides propped up with mammoth tusks, feeding bones into an open fire. Reindeer and musk ox roamed the chilly turf outside.

As of five thousand years ago, remarkable changes had begun to take place in the region. The climate had warmed, the great wild herds were depleted or gone; agriculture was displacing hunting and the gathering of wild foods. In the area just north of the Black Sea, in the western Ukraine and in Rumania, the people of the Tripolye culture still used stone tools. But their way of life had changed dramatically from that of the earlier hunting culture. The Tripolye people grew crops; they had domestic animals. Their dwellings often had several rooms, probably with a family to each. Clay floors were laid in these rooms and then fired to make them hard, before the rest of the structure went up. In each room, taking perhaps a quarter or a fifth of the floor space, stood a large clay oven.

With the spread of agriculture similar clay and stone ovens appeared all over east, north, and central Europe. "With time," as Alfred Faber wrote, "the peasant's clay stove . . . developed into the real heat source of the house. It stood in the main room as a huge lump or box-shaped structure. . . . It was used for cooking, roasting, baking, drying fruit; around it children grew up, the peasant and his family slept on the stove's roof, and he died there. Beneath the stove fowl hatch, pigs root, and suckling pigs

Figure 92 Massive clay oven used three to five thousand years ago in the Ukraine, by people of the Tripolye culture. The clay floors of dwellings like this may also have been hardened by fire during construction.

grow fat." Faber wrote about Germany, but his words apply over the whole area where such ovens came into use. They appeared in Germany and Poland about four thousand years ago, and in the Ukraine a bit earlier. They seem to have worked their way up from the south, coming into common use in Europe with the spread of agriculture.

The great masonry ovens of north, east, and central Europe form a distinct class among the world's heating devices. When Tolstoy writes that "Pahon, the master of the house, was lying on top of the stove . . ." the north American reader knows he is in a different realm. The stove that can be slept upon is not a part of his heritage. The idea would be familiar in the Far East or in Egypt, but not in Britain or France.

THE PEASANT OVEN

There is a tendency in the West to lump the massive ovens of the east collectively as "Russian stoves." Russian literature has, inadvertently, helped the notion along. But old Russia is but one among many locations where clay and brick stoves have been used. They are the traditional heating devices also of Rumania, Hungary, the Ukraine, Poland, Yugoslavia, Byelorussia, Lithuania, Latvia, Estonia, Karelia, and Finland. The style of peasant ovens has varied somewhat from region to region in this part of the world, but in a basic sense they are everywhere the same. Each is a multipurpose device occupying a central place in life and in the dwelling—for cooking, heating, drying food or garments, sometimes for firing pottery or for the sauna. Usually the old or children were given the warmest sleeping place on the stove

Figures 93 (top) and 94   East European clay ovens with sleeping area and benches for sitting. Figure 93 from Hungary, figure 94 from Poland.

top. Others slept nearby on benches or platforms. Planks covered with straw often lay over the brick surface used for sleeping.

The peasant's clay or brick stove could be a device of considerable beauty. The architectural quality of some later ovens—massive affairs with one or more ovens for baking, stairs leading to a sleeping platform, cooking areas, spark hoods, candle niches, drying niches—could be outstanding. Some were beautifully decorated with tiles. Others had elaborate designs painted on them. (I had hoped to have a photograph of a Polish oven with floral designs; political events seem to have derailed that possibility for the present.)

But many of the traditional ovens, perhaps most of them, tended to be rather crudely made, great lumps standing in the middle of the room, as Faber put it. Some of these ovens were of stone; these were common in the north, the east Baltic, Sweden, and Finland. Many were of clay, carefully prepared for use and then packed down hard with mallets during construction. In more recent times the more prosperous peasant could afford brick, or even decorative tiles. Even so stoves made with skill and care, and which offered better performance, were probably the exception rather than the rule in the peasant household. John Paget, traveling in Hungary and Transylvania in the mid-1800s, found that the stoves required regular repair, "especially at the com-

mencement of winter." Although Paget did not elaborate, very likely he referred to cracks developed because of poor construction or incompatible materials. Right up into the twentieth century, peasant stoves continued to be built in some rural areas without any chimney, or perhaps only with a hood that blocked sparks or carried smoke only as far as the attic.

Wood was the standard fuel in the clay oven. Peat or straw came into use where wood was scarce. One of the most distinctive of the straw-burners was the *bubos kemence* of the Hungarian plains or steppe region. *Kemence* means oven, and *bubos* means stack or tuft, reflecting the haystack shape of the oven. The fuel burned in it might be hay, reeds, or the dried stalks of plants. Sometimes it was manure mixed with straw, formed into square cakes and then dried. The villagers made their own ovens, forming a frame of poles and interwoven branches and then plastering over the frame with clay. The method is thousands of years old and continues in use in some parts of the world today.

Typically the clay oven of east Europe was fueled from the room in which it stood. The bubos kemence was an exception; the oven stood in the living room, but one side lay against the kitchen wall and the fuel door was in the kitchen. This made it possible to keep smoke and the litter from fuel out of the living area. Central Europeans followed a similar practice.

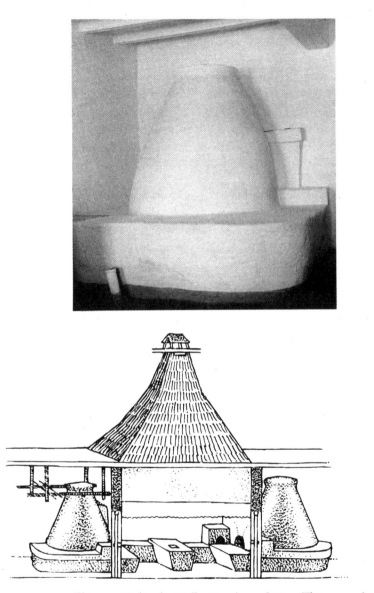

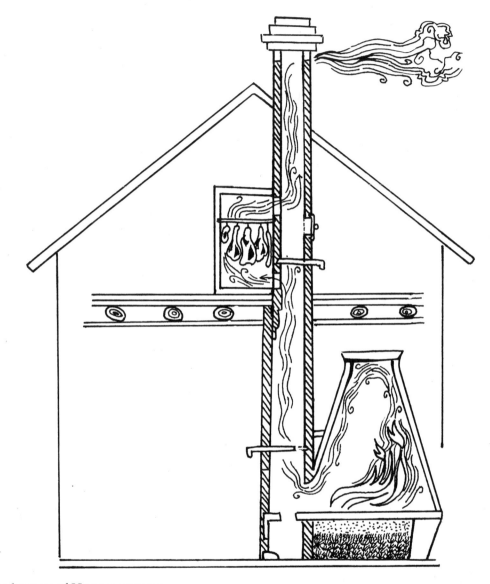

Figures 95 (top), 96 (bottom), and 97 The grass-burning *bubos kemence* of Hungary seems remarkably similar in style to Tripolye ovens built five thousand years ago. But the *bubos kemence* is fired from an adjoining room, the kitchen. (See figure 96). By adjusting dampers, the *bubos kemence* could also be used to smoke meat in an upper chamber.

Firing depended on prosperity, according to Prof. Ildikó Kríza-Horváth, who provided this Hungarian material for me. If you had ample fuel you fired once a day but with enough fuel so that the oven would radiate heat for twenty-four hours. If you had less fuel you fired in late afternoon for evening warmth; or you fired briefly in the morning for cooking, and briefly late in the day to heat the room. Either way, your oven never got as warm as the prosperous peasant's did. The size of the bubos kemence depended on the amount of bread to be baked in it. The biggest ovens could handle seven or eight big, round loaves weighing fifteen to twenty pounds; the smaller ovens took three loaves.

The size of an oven also reflected heating needs. The colder the region, the more massive the oven. It is not just a question of providing an oven large enough for adequate heat, though that's important. More heat means a bigger fire; the more heat, the more stress on the masonry; the more masonry, the more that stress is spread and the effect of it diminished. Size, then, becomes a factor in reducing strain on the stove in regions where heating requirements are great.

The idea that some sort of elf or spirit inhabited the stove was widespread in the past. In Russia this creature was called the *domovoi*, a kind of protective ancestral spirit, friendly but inclined to be mischievous. The family made food offerings to the domovoi and if they moved from one house to another, took the trouble to inform him: "The sleigh is ready for you, go with us." Embers were carried along as well to start the new stove with fire from the old.

Fire was built at the back of the oven, and smoke emerged at its mouth. In Russia there was likely to be a double door at the mouth. The outer door covered the opening completely; the inner door did not quite cover it and there was space at the top for smoke to pass out. During firing, only the inner door was shut. Cooking procedure involved letting the fire burn down to coals, then placing the food inside. Special poles with a U-shaped fork at the end were used to lift and place earthenware pots in the hot interior. Another special pole was used for lifting skillets. Once the food was inside, then the oven door could be closed and the heat retained. From the front face of the Russian stove wall emerged a small pipe that led into the chimney, if there was a chimney. This was the smoke outlet for the samovar, used to make hot water for tea. The samovar had a hollow tube in its center, containing a charcoal fire.

Figure 98 Masonry stove in the Slavonian region of Yugoslavia, 1942. Photo by Erika Groth-Schmachtenberger.

Figure 99 Child's bed by a tile stove in Rumania, 1939. Photo by Erika Groth-Schmachtenberger.

DESIGN IMPROVEMENTS

Like virtually all early stoves, clay ovens were not terribly efficient. The advent of the chimney made the situation worse by channeling even more heat outdoors. This sometimes led to the black stove/white stove combination previously mentioned. Blocking the chimney with a damper, to reduce the heat loss, also became common practice. Once the fire had been reduced to coals, the damper could be shut and the heat kept in. Closing the damper prematurely, of course, could force lethal gases back into the dwelling, with sometimes fatal results.

Just when stove design began to improve in east Europe is not as clear to me as it might be. The best evidence I've found suggests that improvement began as elsewhere, soon after the onset of the Little Ice Age, and that new ideas came

Figure 100   This is the traditional Russian stove familiar from Tolstoy and other Russian writers. At left behind the chimney is a sleeping area. Below are niches where wet gloves can be dried.

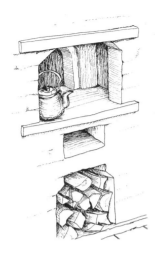

Figure 101 Traditional Russian stove has an outer and an inner door, with smoke rising between into the chimney flue.

In northeast Europe generally the improved stoves of the well-to-do were built in a strongly vertical mode, tall and with long vertical smoke channels. One of the reasons given, by the Russians, for example, is that such smoke channels are more easily cleaned than horizontal passages. The peasant stoves of the region were in time improved as well, but for a long while many of them tended to reflect in shape their origin as ovens; they were broader and lower. Some of the accompanying illustrations, including two based on drawings by the late Jaan Jaakson, demonstrate this.

Jaakson grew up in rural Estonia, using stoves of the type shown in figure

106. "In normal winter weather," he wrote in *Wood Burning Quarterly* in 1976, "a good armful of logs about two feet long, or a bundle or two of twigs, was burned every afternoon and the stove remained warm until the next midday. In severe temperatures of up to 40° below zero, two firings in a 24-hour period were required. The building of a new stove was of some public interest and speculation on the skills of the mason. But the shrewd expert mostly outsmarted the critical bystanders. A new stove sometimes did not draw, unless the [builder] received from the owner his traditional bottle of vodka." One way of ensuring that the stove did not draw un-

from the west. The Russian *Encyclopedic Dictionary* (St. Petersburg, 1898) reports the appearance of "Dutch stoves" in the houses of the well-to-do toward the end of the sixteenth century. These were masonry heat-storage stoves named, I believe, for glazed Dutch tiles decorating the exterior, rather than for the origin of the stove itself. "At the termination of combustion," says the dictionary, "if some coals still remain in the fuel box, this flue is closed by dampers, usually in the attic, employing special sliding doors." The Dutch stoves channeled smoke through several long horizontal or vertical passages, up one, down the next, and so on. The dictionary indicates that they were not very efficient, until Russian designers began making improvements early in the nineteenth century.

Figures 102 and 103 Two examples of massive stoves used in the far north. These stoves were built in Finland, but similar types occur in adjoining areas of the U.S.S.R.

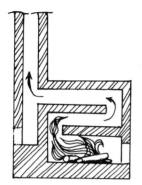

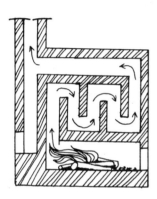

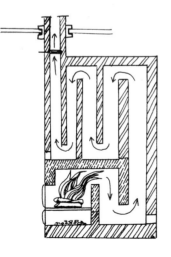

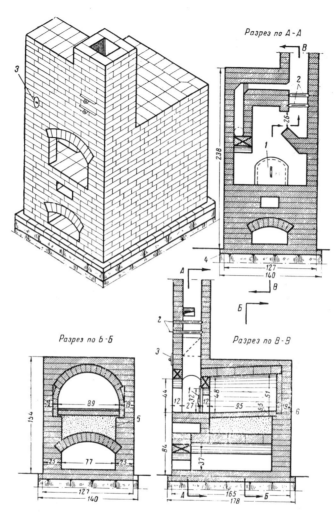

Figure 107 Improved version of traditional Russian stove.

Figures 104 (top), 105 (center), and 106 (bottom) Masonry heating stoves from Estonia described by Jaan Jaakson. Jaakson found the type shown in figure 106 to be more effective than the other two, which are older.

til the builder intended was to block a flue. Then, when the mason had been paid and had his vodka, he could clear the flue and presto, the stove would work.

In Latvia, according to Pauls Kundzins, stove builders sometimes looped smoke channels from the stove beneath a masonry bench, or even under a section of the floor. The bench heated by smoke from the stove is common in central Europe.

In Russia, stove improvements in more recent times have taken two forms: (1) an effort to modify the traditional peasant's stove, basically a modified form of the old multipurpose clay oven; and (2) efforts to perfect a tall vertical-channel stove intended entirely for heating.

The drawings in figure 107 show a version of the traditional peasant stove. Little has been done here in the way of improvement except to build of brick, and to construct the firebox/oven chamber for maximum heat retention. Note the pitch of the oven floor and roof, designed by its slope to keep gases and heat from rushing up the chimney flue. Dimensions are in centimeters. Numbers on the drawings, other than dimensions, refer to the following:

1. Door to firing-cooking-baking chamber.

2. Dampers (two of them) to close chimney and retain heat.

3. Small flue for samovar.

4. Insulation under base of stove.

5. Mixture of fine gravel and river sand mixed with broken glass, beneath oven floor.

6. Refers to a two-centimeter rise in oven floor, front to back.

Figures 108 and 109 show a more ambitious approach to improving the peasant oven. Here the firebox (access at the left side of the stove) lies beneath the oven. There is a grate as well as a range top for cooking. By opening a damper, smoke can be made to pass directly from the firebox into the chimney. This keeps the stove cooler during summer use. In winter the damper is closed and smoke then passes through the series of vertical flues along the right-hand side of the stove. The stove can be built into a wall, so that the bank of flues on the right warms a second room. Dimensions are in centimeters. Numbered references in the drawings are as follows:

1. Door to oven chamber.

2. Firebox door.

3. Air intake opening below grate.

4. Grate.

5. Range top, in front of oven door.

6. Hot-water reservoir.

7. Vent for range/oven, closed by damper.

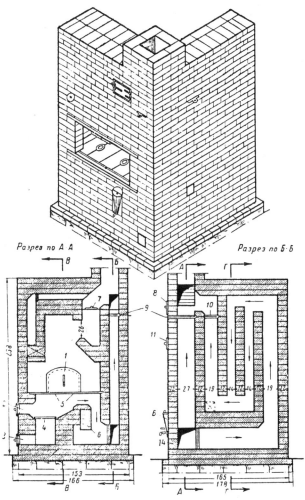

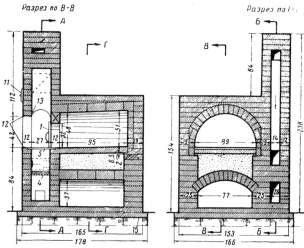

Figures 108 (left) and 109 Traditional Russian stove with a bank of extra heating flues added at one side to improve efficiency.

8. Door giving access to vent.

9. Damper, open for summer, closed for winter.

10. Damper, closed for summer, open for winter.

11. Samovar outlet.

12. Metal covering for opening to range area on face of stove.

13. Angle iron set into brick at opening to range area.

14. Cleanouts.

15. Insulation at base of stove.

In the 1920s and 1930s in Russia, I.S. Podgorodnikov made an effort to transform the peasant stove. He wanted to preserve the original functions of cooking, baking, drying food, and heating. He also wanted to achieve very high efficiency. He built and tested stoves, and kept improving his design. Finally he announced a model that he said could be operated at an efficiency of 85 percent. He called it Teplushka II (figures 110 and 111).

Podgorodnikov took the fire out of the oven and put it in a box with a grate on the left side of the stove. From there the hot gases moved up through the oven, then down through four channels on the oven's right side to a chamber below.

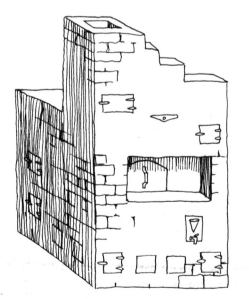

Figures 110 (left) and 111 Podgorodnikov's stove.

From this chamber the smoke made its way forward to the chimney flue and out. The inventor's tests showed gases entering the chimney at 125° to 150°C (257° to 302°F), and leaving the chimney at 110°C (230°F). This compares favorably with the more efficient central European stoves being made today. The stove burned a variety of fuels: wood, peat, straw, and coal. There was a grate and combustion air came from below. Dampers made it possible to bypass the lower heat chamber for summer use. Detailed drawings for the stove run more than thirty pages and could not be included here.

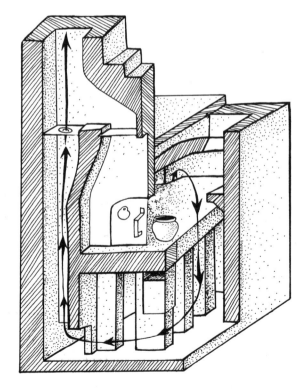

All over Europe with the passage of time, stoves became more specialized. Dwellings grew larger; rooms acquired special functions. All-purpose clay ovens were in the process transformed into separate devices for cooking, heating, or baking. The heating stoves of north and east Europe tended, as noted, to be tall ones.

To the uninitiated, the variety of channel patterns used in these stoves may seem bewildering. It is probably fair to say that if you can imagine a channel pattern, it has been built somewhere, sometime, by someone. The schematic drawings in figure 112 suggest only some among the patterns tried out in Russia alone. Figures 179 through 182 in the appendix show how a few of these patterns have been carried out in brick heating stoves. These particular stoves are heavy-weights, built by masonry specialists and weighing two to three tons each. They could be designed to burn wood, coal, or peat.

In the 1930s and 1940s, however, the U.S.S.R. needed one million to two million new stoves a year. It proved difficult to provide this many heavy-weight brick models built to high standards. Also, massive stoves did not fit in with the kind of housing being put up at the time. Big stoves required a lot of support and this created structural problems. So there was an effort to mass-produce lighter-weight one-ton stoves. It was an ambitious undertaking, which may hold ideas useful to us today in North America.

The goal was to simplify construction, to create mass-produced components that could be put together swiftly on the site with a minimum of skill. The new stoves were to retain the heat-storage principle. The interior was to be of brick, but the walls were to be thinner and the overall mass reduced. Surface temperatures ran higher compared to the older and more massive stoves; they had to in order to provide an equivalent heat output. Still surface temperatures remained far below those of iron models.

Mass-produced masonry stoves came in several forms. The most desirable, apparently, were those made of big tiles. The tiles were laid up one on top of the other as with chimney block except that the finished product was a stove and not a chimney. The difficulty was that tile production could not meet demand. So other stoves were made of concrete block, again made and laid up like chimney block. Clay mortar and special fire-resistant concrete were used (figure 178).

A third type of mass-produced stove, evidently the most common, was made of brick covered with sheet metal or with an asbestos board veneer (figure 177). This had a steel frame. Similar stoves have long been used in Finland and in the east Baltic area (Lithuania, Latvia, Estonia). G. E. Asp, a keen student of masonry stoves writing in the 1940s, felt that sheet-metal-covered brick stoves produced in Finland were among the most successful masonry stoves of any kind.

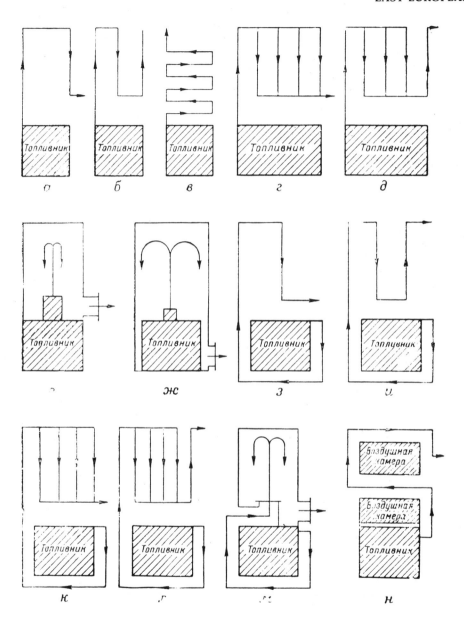

Figure 112 Sample smoke channel patterns from Russian stoves. Where several arrows point downward together, it indicates that smoke flows down through all channels simultaneously into a common channel below. The area indicated by slanting lines is the firebox.

Chapter
9

Swedish Stoves

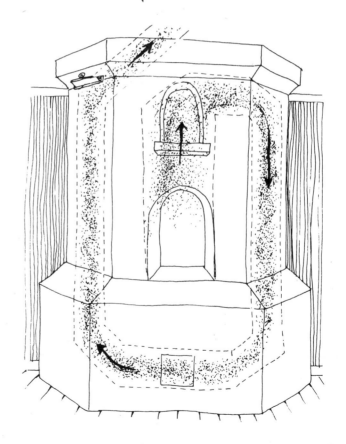

During the eighteenth century Sweden grew worried about its wood supply, fearing the profound effect that a shortage might have on the country. This concern reflected a condition that developed over wide areas of Europe during the first energy crisis, though with variations as to timing and intensity of concern. For two reasons, however, the Swedish experience stands out: first, the speed of transition to improved stoves, once the process got well underway; second, the general excellence of the new stoves. These quickly gained a reputation as the best in Europe.

As the eighteenth century began, open fires remained the primary source of heat in Sweden as they had since prehistoric times. Traditional Swedish fireplaces are particularly graceful and distinctive, usually standing in one corner of a room rather than at the center of a wall. They were superior fireplaces, in that they had dampers to hold heat in after the fire died. But like all fireplaces the Swedish models consumed enormous amounts of wood. Their peak efficiency has been put at 10 percent, a drab level shared by most fireplaces the world over.

Tile stoves appeared in Sweden during medieval times. The idea traveled north from Germany, but for a long time it failed to take hold in Scandinavia. These early stoves may have been more effective than fireplaces, but not by any vast margin. They lacked interior smoke channels to extract the heat, which moved directly from the firebox into the chimney. The masonry walls of the stove were thick, and acted to insulate the room from the fire's warmth. A visitor to Stockholm reported in 1720 that he had to begin firing his stove in the morning to get the room warm by evening, "but still I am cold!" The question of heat transfer to the room was one the early tile-stove builders all but failed to deal with. This was surely a factor in the early rarity of these stoves in Sweden. Where they were used, often they stood in the same room with the fireplace, serving only as supplementary heaters at night after the open fire died.

SAVING THE FOREST

So long as there was plenty of wood, there was little incentive in Sweden to do away with the open fireplace. One important reason was illumination, which the fireplace provided more conveniently than did other common lighting methods of the time. Rush lights required time and labor to prepare, and oil for lamps had to be produced from animal fat or fish. The fire was a necessity for warmth; its light was free and required no extra labor. And this light was essential to perform tasks after dark.

In the long northern winters firelight, of course, assumes a special role. Dawn comes late; dusk arrives in early afternoon and the brief interval between is often gray with clouds. The dark months

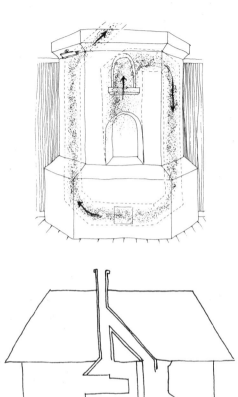

Figures 113 (top) and 114 In Sweden and Finland heat storage fireplaces came into use long ago. A damper (upper left) blocked the chimney flue to hold heat in after the fire died. The stove at far right on the cover of this book began as such a fireplace; the doors were added later. Figure 114 shows the location of this particular stove in a Swedish farmhouse. Construction is of brick covered with plaster. Backed up against the stove in the next room, and sharing a common chimney, is a big cooking/baking complex. Stove and cooking/baking complex together form a warm masonry mass at the center of the house. Drawings after Bengt Carlén.

are difficult to bear even without the element of cold, and since prehistoric times fire has been both symbol and surrogate for the sun in northern lands. In heavily forested regions like Sweden it was only natural to use firewood liberally. The French diarist Charles Ogier, writing in Stockholm during a cold winter (1634), said that "nowhere have I spent such an agreeable winter. We had such a lot of wood to dispose of that it was particularly easy to keep the cold away. I remember that d'Avangour, who is wasteful by nature, never entered the room where we had our meals without throwing another bundle of wood on the burning fire."

But just a century later there is concern about the wood supply. In 1739 and 1741 two men, Anders Johan Nordenberg and N. Brelin, reported to the Swedish Academy of Science on attempts to improve the tile stove. The improvements were required, they said, "particularly to save the forests for the future, as we have seen them diminish in a remarkable way." Wood was then the chief construction material in Sweden. It was the fuel for dwelling, foundry, and forge, in fact for all manufactures. Demand was expanding from the increased population.

Early efforts to improve the tile stove were something less than a rousing success. The designs in figure 115 show ingenuity and understanding of a major difficulty, the need to improve heat transfer. But these and other early "im-

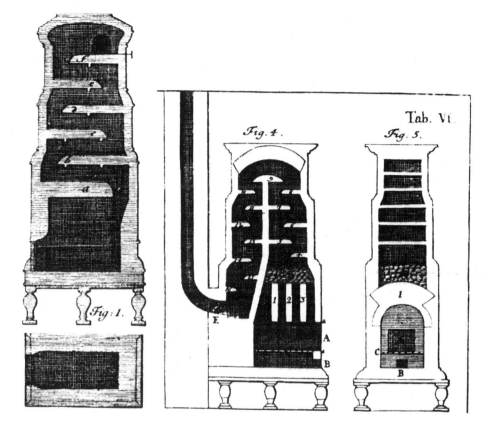

Figure 115 Two early eighteenth century efforts to design more efficient stoves in Sweden.

provements" in the masonry stove were never widely used. Today it remains uncertain whether this was because of weaknesses in design, high cost, or resistance to new ideas. Very likely all three factors were at work.

Concern about the wood supply continued to mount. There were even efforts to stimulate the building of stone rather than timber houses. Then in 1767 the Swedish government decided to take a hand; the king sought the help of a well-

known architect, Baron Carl Johan Cronstedt, in designing stoves that would burn less wood. Cronstedt in turn enlisted the aid of a general, Baron Fabian Wrede, known already for his work on stove design. The king's request came in January and by the fall of 1767 Cronstedt delivered a report that included plans for several stoves—stoves for heating, cooking, baking, roasting, even for cooking cattle feed and for heating irons to press clothing. What the designs had in com-

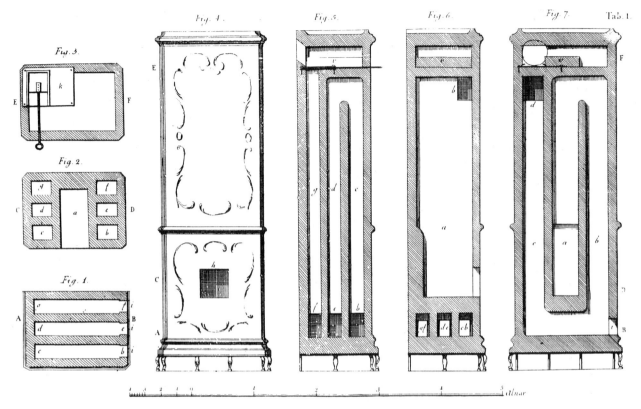

Figure 116 This is a seven-channel stove from the collection of designs by barons Cronstedt and Wrede. In these stoves the smoke travels consecutively through channels marked in lower case letters, *a, b, c,* and so on. The channel marked *a* rises from the firebox. The smoke then descends through channel *b*, rises through *c*, descends through *d*, and so on. The device marked *k* is a sliding damper used to close off the chimney flue. Cleanouts, located at the bottom of the stove and shown in figure 1, are marked *i*. The cross-hatched area labeled *h* is the fuel door. The scale of measure shown is in *aln*, an obsolete Swedish measure equivalent to .594 meters or 23.39 inches.

mon was that they were, so far as I can determine, unmatched anywhere at that period for a combination of beauty, efficiency, and general elegance. They seemed then and they remain today a truly remarkable achievement, and there

is little doubt that some of them would rank well today in a stove efficiency contest. I showed one of these two-hundred-fifty-year-old designs to a master stove builder with wide experience in central and eastern Europe and he felt it

would compare well in efficiency with anything being built at present.

Cronstedt was no naive experimenter. He knew what he was about and why. "Our woodlands are so reduced," he wrote, "that there is fear that fuel will be insufficient. We must abolish heavy wood consumption." The older tile stoves, he complained, had doors that were too big. Big doors offered the pleasure of seeing the fire and using its light, said Cronstedt, but they were not efficient: "The useful must be put before the pleasant." Dampers on the old stoves were no good; they let too much heat up the chimney. As another student of the older masonry stoves said, "You lit fires for the birds."

The Cronstedt/Wrede approach was to channel hot gases from the firebox so that they traveled up and down through a series of vertical passages within the stove. As they moved through these passages, the gases lost their heat to the masonry, whence it made its way into the room. The heat transfer problem was solved. The stoves were designed to be made either of tile (in which case the standard central European tile construction technique was used) or of brick. The brick stoves were plastered and whitewashed, and they were cheaper to build.

Cronstedt and Wrede made other changes in the older tile stoves. These had had such large fireboxes, Cronstedt believed, that there was a tendency to build outsize fires and so crack the masonry. So in the new models the firebox size was reduced; a smaller box warmed up more quickly and thus combustion efficiency improved. The size of firebox doors also came down; this reduced air movement through the stove and improved heat transfer.

Cold air, the Baron noted, collects on the floor of every room. He designed channels into some of his stoves through which this cool air could move as through a chimney, to be warmed and then recirculated to the room. Our air-circulating fireplaces and circulator stoves use the same approach today. "When building the air channels you must recognize," wrote Cronstedt, "that the thinner they can be made, the better, and the more rapidly they will take and deliver warmth. For this I have had a potter make thin bricks, lapped on the uppermost and lower edges, so that all cross-joints can be made strong and tight, which is rather important so that no smoke may slip in from the smoke channel, in which case an inconvenient smell would enter the room." (See figure 117.)

Baron Cronstedt urged those who used his stoves to split their fuel-wood fine. He wanted them to use small pieces, of uniform size, so that the pieces would all burn down to coals together. Then the damper could be shut and the heat kept in. Fuel of mixed sizes meant that the large pieces would burn longer, and the damper had to be left open until they were consumed, with consequent

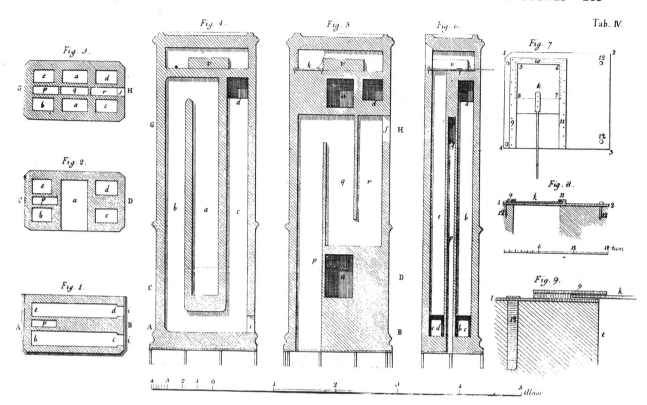

Figure 117   This is a Cronstedt/Wrede stove with five smoke channels, *a*, *b*, *c*, *d*, and *e*. Three additional channels, *p*, *q*, and *r*, warm air from the room. The cool air from the floor enters channel *p* at the bottom of the stove, passes down through channel *q*, rises through *r*, and then exits, warmed, into the room again. Drawings at the right in this figure show the construction of the sliding damper.

heat loss up the chimney. The Baron was a meticulous and painstaking man who turned his attention to the least detail. Modern tile stove builders offer the same advice on fuel size today.

As to efficiency, Cronstedt compared one of his new models over a period of nine weeks with an old-style stove. He found that the old stove used 2.71 times

more wood to provide equivalent heat. And that, he said in modest understatement, "all makes for substantial economizing of wood, and more than I could expect."

No doubt some of the Cronstedt/Wrede designs had their flaws. Hot gases moved consecutively through the long vertical smoke channels. This tend-

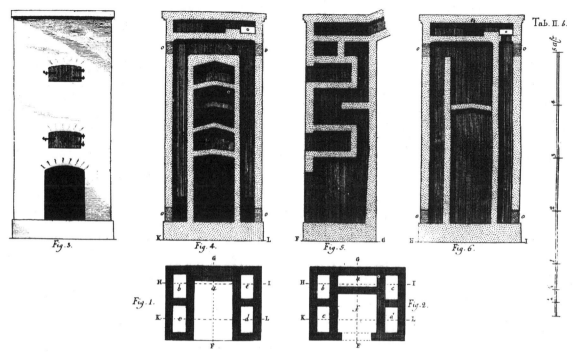

Figure 118   This Cronstedt/Wrede model is a five-channel brick design, with two baking or warming ovens labeled *f*. Channel pattern is similar to that in other Cronstedt/Wrede designs, except that channel *a* follows an irregular route to get around the ovens. The points marked *o* in figures 4 and 6 indicate bricks that can be removed to provide access for cleaning.

ed to make for uneven heating of the stove's surface area, an effect that designers today try to minimize. The Baron reported it "very possible" that the cleanouts built into his stoves would indeed have to be used to remove soot. So presumably combustion was not always as complete as it might have been, at least in certain models and conditions. Without testing, it is difficult to tell whether such a defect is more the fault of the de-

sign or of the stove's operator; more often it is the latter. Failing to build a sufficiently hot fire can of itself cause difficulty. The tile stoves in use today in Sweden are descendants and near relations of the old Cronstedt/Wrede designs, and I'm told that they show no particular soot problems. So quite possibly human failings were the major cause of soot buildup in the Baron's time, as they often are today.

Human failing was the source of another difficulty that Cronstedt foresaw and planned for. Tile stoves are heavy. Where not adequately supported below, their weight may cause the floor to settle. The side of the stove farthest from the wall settles most as a rule, because support there tends to be least. The stove thus tilts away from the wall, its top moving most and the bottom least. Where the pipe connecting stove and chimney is at the top of the stove, it suffers maximum damage; located at the bottom of the stove it suffers least. Therefore, said Cronstedt, locate the chimney pipe connector low down at the rear of the stove—sound advice today.

The King of Sweden was an early customer for one of the new tile stoves, and others in the social hierarchy followed. Wooden models were built to show potters, who made the tiles and were thus the stove builders of that era, how the new stoves were put together. Finally there was the book with detailed drawings in 1775. All this was part of a government plan to get the new stoves into widespread use and so to conserve wood fuel. In the next quarter century, the new designs spread throughout Sweden. Production began in Denmark as well. By 1798 the Italian traveler Giuseppe Acerbi could remark that "The stoves in Sweden are the most ingeniously contrived of any in Europe for heating a chamber and keeping it warm with a very small quantity of wood."

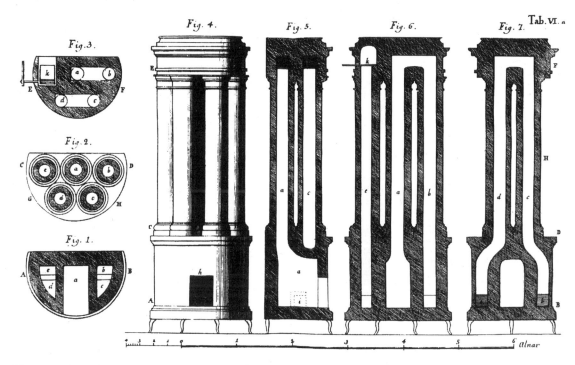

Figure 119 This Cronstedt/Wrede design is a five-channeled stove with columns, which provided more heat-radiating surface and so improved efficiency. In figures 3 and 6, *k* represents the sliding damper. The smoke path is up channel *a*, down *b*, up *c*, and so on to the chimney.

The Swedish designs seem never to have spread to Germany, which developed its own improved stoves. But in 1806 a German-language technological encyclopaedia (Krunitz) stated that, "We know that the average winter cold in Sweden is unusually severe, and yet there may be no other country where man has reached the goal of protecting himself against the severity of the season at so little expense." Some very beautiful tile stoves were at this time being made in Austria, Germany, Switzerland, and elsewhere in central Europe. The German encyclopaedist evidently did not feel they measured up to the Swedish models.

Today Sweden no longer manufactures stove tiles. The last tile factories closed down in the 1920s and there are perhaps two dozen practicing tile stove builders in the whole country, who repair and rebuild old stoves. The only "new" tile stoves available in Sweden are antiques salvaged from old buildings. These stoves may be a century and more old, but rebuilt they are as good as new.

Today's common Swedish tile stove is a five-channel model, a workaday modification of the old Cronstedt/Wrede designs. A Swedish reference book rates the efficiency at 70 to 80 percent. Ratings for some of the more complex (i.e. nine-

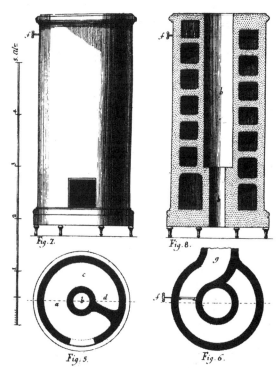

Figure 120 In this round stove the smoke moved upward from the firebox, *a*, in a spiral pattern to the damper, *f*. The channel *b* in the center of the stove carried room air and increased the radiating surface.

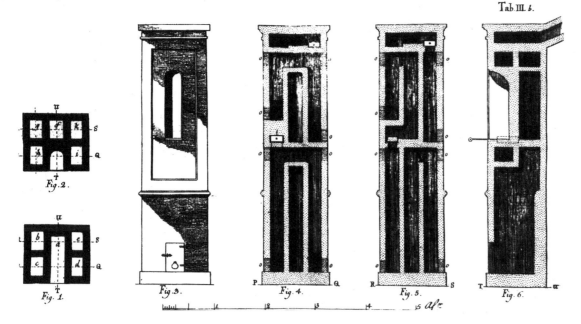

Tab III. b.

Fig. 2.

Fig. 1.

Fig. 3.

Fig. 4.

Fig. 5.

Fig. 6.

Figure 121 This Cronstedt/Wrede stove could be called a ten-channel model. Smoke passed consecutively through channels *a, b, c, d,* and *e* on the stove's lower level, and then through *f, g, h, i,* and *k* on the upper level. There are two dampers, one on the lower level at the top of channel *e,* and another atop channel *k* on the level above. The niche at the front of the stove (figure 3) probably held a candle for lighting.

channel) Cronstedt/Wrede designs could well have been higher. Apparently they were never tested, and in later years Swedish builders settled for a standard five-channel design, which was effective enough and simpler to build.

DAMPERS CAN BE LETHAL

Dampers are a prosaic subject, little-pursued in stove literature. But they can be lethal devices and are on the whole best discussed. Baron Cronstedt gave the subject some thought, so this is perhaps a good place to discuss them.

There are two schools of thought in Europe as regards dampers. Sweden, Finland, Russia, and some other eastern countries are of the full-closure school. That is, when the fire in the stove burns down, the Swedes and those who think as they do close a damper that entirely blocks the smoke passage between the stove and chimney. Obviously it makes sense to do this only if there is no more smoke, and the object is to keep the heat in. The objective seems reasonable; most

of the masonry stoves built in the U.S. to date have been built with such dampers, generally a flat plate that slides horizontally to close the opening into the chimney.

However, what the Swedes, Finns, and Russians do with their dampers as a matter of routine, the Germans, Swiss, and Austrians prohibit by law. In the tile stoves of those countries, you may not build a damper that closes more than 80

Figure 122 Wooden model of Cronstedt/Wrede stove, used to show potters how to construct them.

percent of the way. The remaining 20 percent of the flue passage *must* remain open always. Most stove builders allow an even larger margin, say two-thirds closure. Often they install no dampers at all. The Swedes, the Finns, and the Russians are concerned about keeping heat inside the building. The Germans, Swiss, and Austrians fear that blocking the chimney may cause fumes to back up and asphyxiate citizens.

Neither school wishes to waste heat, of course; and both schools claim efficiency levels approaching the maximum generally considered feasible, 85 percent or thereabouts. Looking a bit more closely, then, this is what one finds: The Swedes *must* have a full-closure damper because the doors of their tile stoves are not airtight. If the damper remained open after the fire died, there would be a draft through the stove that would carry off heat to be lost. The central Europeans take great pains to have their stoves and the doors airtight. I used a German model last winter with a door that torqued down so tightly I would not have hesitated to submerge in it as in a bathysphere. The idea, of course, is that if air can't get into the stove it can't move through it and carry off heat. This is a vital matter in the design of masonry stoves, and the two schools of damper design simply take different approaches to it. Presumably there is some slight movement of cool air down the flue (and of warm air up and out) in the central European types. But to judge by their ef-

ficiency figures, the loss of heat can't be very great. So both methods seem to work well.

What are the risks of the full-closure damper? Apparently it has been a source of trouble in Russia in the past, to what degree I cannot say. Stories from the old days tell of asphyxiated peasants, as well as of asphyxiated aristocrats whose servants impatiently (or drunkenly or irritably) closed the damper too soon. There have been problems in Finland as well, though how extensive I can't say. Still the Swedes seem not to have suffered much from their closed dampers. Björn-Erik Lindblom, a writer and stove expert who looked into the situation for me in Sweden, found no suggestion of serious difficulty. And the Italian traveler Acerbi, who thought so highly of Swedish stoves, remarked on this in 1798. Swedish stoves, he said, "are rather dangerous in the hands of strangers. But the Swedes know so exactly the moment when it is fit to close the air hole (chimney damper) that there is scarcely an instance of any accident happening from the use of stoves in Sweden."

This seemed so striking that I asked Björn to find out more about it, and he described as follows an old Swedish method of regulating the damper to conserve heat: As the fire subsides, the idea is to close the damper as much as possible, a bit at a time until the fire is out and the damper can be shut entirely. The trick is in knowing how much to shut it at any given moment without causing

Figures 123 and 124 The typical Swedish stove remaining in use today is a five-channel model. Figure 123 shows the exterior of such a stove. (Courtesy of Nordiska Museet). Figure 124 shows the interior.

fumes to enter the room. (By then of course the fire is at the charcoal stage and there is no visible smoke.) Well, you put your cheek close against the stove tiles just above the fuel door and start closing the damper, sniffing briskly all

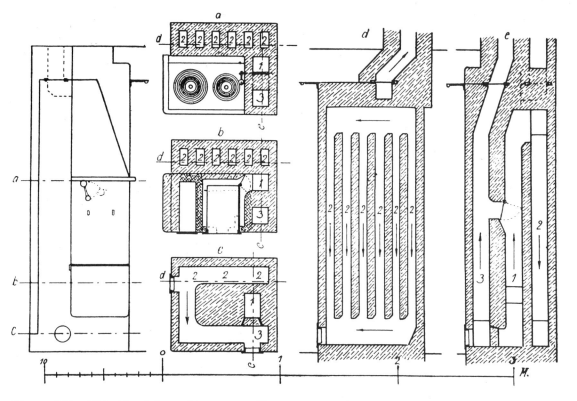

Figure 125 This Finnish cooking range illustrates a technique used also in Russia, the heat-storage battery wall. Here a damper permits smoke to leave the range and go straight into the chimney flue (3) in summer. In winter the smoke is directed into another flue (1) and then downward through six parallel flues (2) simultaneously before moving into the chimney flue (3). Sometimes the chimney itself is laced with vertical flues and used as a storage battery.

put it mildly, is not a culture where all are attuned to the precise and careful handling of mechanical devices, even where risks are involved. But if my head says close it 80 percent, my heart is with the old man in Sweden, who can tell with his nose how to run his stove, and who needs no government regulations to look out for his own life, or the lives of others.

One further thing should be said here about the flat, horizontal slide dampers commonly used in stoves: If these dampers are not properly made, in time they will stick. American stove builders are already running into the problem. The damper is encased in several tons of brick and mortar, and it can indeed be frustrating to have it stick. Fortunately Baron Cronstedt took this question in hand two hundred fifty years ago, and believed he had the solution, which involves building the slide damper so that bits of soot, fly ash, mortar and brick cannot invade the mechanism and cause it to bind. An illustration of the Baron's damper is shown in figure 117.

the while. The moment you detect fumes escaping, you back off on the damper, opening it just enough so that the fumes stop. Björn received this lore from an elderly gentleman, a longtime tile stove user. "To shut the damper by this method is to be warm and safe, he told me, and he is an old and vital man."

In America partisans of the 80 percent closure and full-closure dampers will one day have it out, probably with code people joining in the fray. I agree strongly with the 80 percent folk, for I've seen how little attention some people can give to their stoves, to say nothing of their safety and that of other people. Ours, to

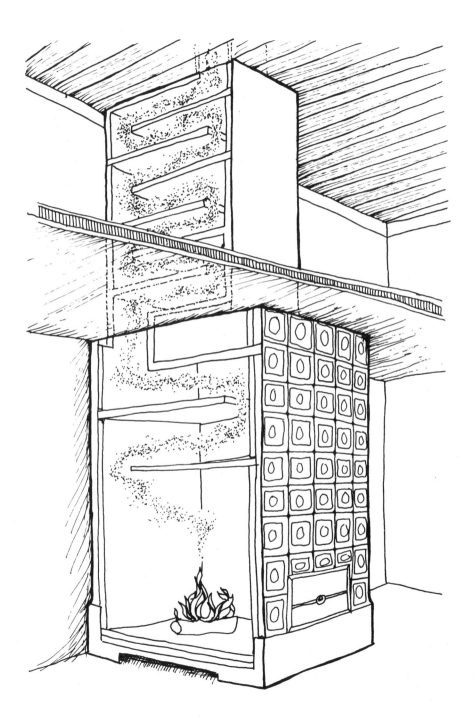

Chapter
10
Central
European
Stoves

The tile stoves of central Europe are surely among the most spectacular heating devices ever made. Many are exhibited in palaces and museums today as works of art, particularly in Austria, Switzerland, and Germany. The uninitiated sometimes pass them by unaware they are looking at something intended to warm

Figure 126 White stove with gold trim in the Hofburg, the Imperial Palace in Vienna.

Figure 127 Stove in the form of a peasant woman, from Austria. The fuel loading door would be in the wall in the next room.

the room. In the imperial palace at Vienna there are stoves that look rather like gilded vanilla ice cream cones. In a nearby museum the large and colorful figure of a peasant woman, bearing a basket of fruit on her head, is also a stove. Clay as a stove-building material offers infinite possibilities in shape and style.

For years a few New York dealers have imported antique tile stoves to sell to wealthy Americans, who wanted them not to use but to look at. Once in a shop

Figure 128 Stove shaped like the Bastille, from Paris.

I saw such an antique, a round stove about nine feet high with a handsome tile exterior. Inside it there was no firebox, no system of smoke channels; there was nothing to the stove but its exterior shell and the handworked brass doors. "Oh," said the shop's proprietor, "the firebox was taken out. We don't expect to sell it to anyone who would *use* it." The price was $4,000. That was in 1973, before the oil embargo. Today in Switzerland you might easily pay $4,000 or $5,000 for a new tile stove, and it would work very well. But because of the demand you would probably have to join a waiting list. The situation has been similar in Germany and Austria.

In central Europe the craft of tile-stove construction has not died out as it very nearly has in Sweden. Austria, Germany, and Switzerland have brought the masonry stove into the twentieth century; their stove builders have learned to adapt. They design masonry heating systems that use the full range of modern fuels: coal, coke, oil, gas, and electricity as well as wood. They build systems that answer modern demands for warming the entire house rather than a room or two. Today Swiss tile stoves built for baking may provide central heating as well. Stoves adapted for solar heating will probably come next. Some European masonry builders are well aware of the potential.

TILE STOVE HISTORY

The origins of the modern stoves are humble, lying in crude kilns and ovens of the Bronze Age or earlier. One school of thought says that tile stoves derive from the clay and stone ovens of north and east Europe; another that they represent combined Germanic and Roman influence. Very likely both schools carry a measure of the truth; the addition of tile does seem to be a Roman contribution.

It is important to understand that stove tiles are not like ordinary floor or wall tiles, which are flat. Stove tiles are vessels. The earliest ones were round clay pots; today's are usually square or rectangular terra cotta boxes. The bottom of the box is glazed and it faces outward to form the visible face of the stove. The boxes serve a structural function; they are not just decorative. Originally all stove tiles were thrown on a wheel by a potter. Today few potters still ply this trade; most tiles are made in factories. But potters probably developed the first tile stoves and for a long while they were the principal builders.

Figure 129 An Austrian tile stove, located in the Tiroler Volkskunst Museum, in Innsbruck.

Figure 130 Early stove tiles. Left, a round clay "pot" tile. Center, a squared-off tile; this design permitted the entire stove surface to be covered with tile. Today the inner section of the tile (seen in the older rounded form at right) is also squared off, so that the tile has a box shape. In form today's tiles are shaped somewhat like cigar boxes, with the bottom of the box facing outward. The stove tile is a box structure, not a flat slab like a floor tile. The deep indentation in the outer surface of the tile provides more surface for heat radiation.

Two obvious questions arise here: What turned potters into stove builders? Why did stove tiles assume the shape of vessels? As with so many things in the realm of heating, the answer is not entirely clear. Rosemarie Franz, in her book *Der Kachelofen*, has outlined one of the prevailing theories, as follows.

Vessels nested inside one another, drinking glasses for example, tend to form an arc. Roman potters sometimes nested clay pots inside each other in this way to produce the form for constructing an arch, for example to build a kiln or oven. They also nested pots in a spiral to make the form for a dome. Now, kilns and ovens have thick clay walls to keep heat *in*. At some point someone thought to put a clay pot in the oven wall to let heat *out*, and the oven became a stove.

This is an ingenious explanation. But it leaves me with the feeling that there is a simpler answer. I believe this answer has to do with cooking. Simple cooking ranges made of clay are extremely old. Many take the simple L-shaped form of what I've called earlier the protofurnace. (See figure 26.) Fuel gets stuffed in the horizontal portion of the L; the cooking vessel, an earthenware pot, sits in the hole at the top of the vertical portion. The thick clay walls of this range keep the heat of the fire in. The pot lets heat out where it can do some good, in this instance by cooking what is in the pot. Cooking methods of this sort were in use in Europe long before tile stoves. They seem a logical source for the notion that you can let heat out of a clay oven by planting earthenware pots in its side.

In the Alpine areas of Switzerland and Austria it is possible to see how this process may have developed. There in the peasants' ovens, round earthenware pots were set into the clay walls, at first just a few pots, and then more and more of them. Some of these pots were put in with their bottoms facing outward, so that they presented a convex surface to the world. Others were set in the opposite way, so that you could warm your hand in the open mouth of the pot. These bottom-inward pots were the ancestors of concave stove tiles still known today as "fist warmers." As more and more pots were added to the oven wall,

it became logical to change the tile's shape. Square and rectangular shapes made it possible to cover the entire oven surface with tile.

Just when tile stoves first appeared is another matter of some scholarly controversy. The first drawings appear in fourteenth-century Zurich. But these show tile stoves already well along in development, as compared with more primitive ones known from peasant dwellings in

Figure 131 Simple stove of a type often found in the Swiss or Austrian Alps. A wooden sleeping platform lies above the oven-shaped fire chamber. Such stoves were fueled from an adjoining room or from outside the building. The common construction materials were clay and very dense, round stones taken from river beds. Building stoves that will not crack from these materials is today almost a lost art.

the Alps. So the origins seem likely to be earlier, possibly as early as the eighth century, possibly two or three centuries later.

There are basic differences between central European masonry stoves and those of east Europe or Sweden. As noted earlier, Swedish, Finnish, and Russian heating stoves tend to be in a vertical mode, with long up-and-down smoke channels. In contrast central European stoves tend to be broader and lower, perhaps following the pattern of the oven. One should not make too much of this; east European peasant stoves also tended to be broad and low, and vertical models are by no means unknown in central Europe. Still there is a basic trend to be seen: Central European stoves are usually more blocky and low, with horizontal smoke channels more commonly used.

This difference in style is interesting for two reasons: First, because it is there; second, because at least some stove builders have believed horizontal smoke channels provide greater efficiency. Marcus Bull's experiments in the 1820s suggested that, given two stoves with smoke channels of equal length, but with one designed in the horizontal and the other in the vertical mode, the stove with horizontal channels will be a bit more efficient. There doesn't seem to be any logical reason why this should be so, and Mr. Bull's figures could have resulted from error. Still some stove builders have believed it to be true, and built stoves accordingly. Leonidas Gimbutas wrote about it in the 1920s in Lithuania. With due skepticism, then, I pass the idea on for those who may wish to experiment.

Another difference between central Europe and the east has to do with fueling. Swedish and east European stoves are generally fueled from the room that houses the stove, just as with the typical iron stove. Central European stoves are

Figure 132 Stokeholes for fueling stove or oven from another room. These are from Poland, but similar arrangements were widespread over central Europe. Smoke escaped from the two smaller openings above the large stokehole. The room where the stove stood, beyond the wall, remained free of smoke in this way. In modern times fueling from an adjoining room has remained common, but a chimney is now built into the wall.

Figure 133 An Austrian stove in early beehive oven style. Clay pots, the first stove tiles, were set into the thick clay walls of such ovens to let the heat out. Here the pots are used in the convex, or bottom-outward, mode.

almost invariably built with one side backed against a wall; the fuel door is on the other side of that wall. The stove that warms the main living space may be fueled from a hall, from the kitchen, or even from outside the house, but not from the room in which the stove sits. In the days before chimneys came into use, and even afterward, this made an important difference in indoor atmosphere. It eliminated smoke, ash, and the other debris of wood burning from the room

where the family gathered to be warm. It also eliminated the drafts set up by air drawn in to feed the fire. This habit of firing the stove from another room, or from outdoors, may stem from the Roman hypocaust, which was also fueled from an outside furnace. The Romans built many hypocausts in central Europe when their empire extended into that region.

Figure 134 Here the transition has been made to square tiles, covering the entire surface of the stove.

Early central European tile and clay stoves were, like their counterparts elsewhere, "terrible devourers of wood," as Alfred Faber put it. Faber estimated that 70 to 80 percent of the heat was lost with the smoke gases up the chimney. As noted in Part I, this began to change after the arrival of the Little Ice Age in the middle of the sixteenth century. Gradually advances came about in both iron and masonry stoves. There was nothing comparable to the veritable design blitz staged by Cronstedt and Wrede in Sweden. No figure of genius stands out. The stove design contest staged by Frederick the Great in 1763 did produce

Figure 135 Two men and a cat on stove bench in the Austrian Tyrol, 1935. Photo by Erika Groth-Schmachtenberger.

Figure 136 Man putting on dry stockings before his domed clay stove in the Austrian Tyrol, 1940. Note trestle bed at left.

one design, the winning one by Baumer, which has been very widely used since and which remains in use today in iron stoves. Faber also singles out Franz Kessler, a Cologne artist and inventor, as being the first to use baffles to improve heat output. Kessler produced a book on wood-conserving iron and masonry stove designs in 1618.

This slowness of change in central Europe Faber attributes to customs of the time. "The medieval man and especially the craftsman were neither personally nor economically free, and individual rights were unknown. Hindered by guild regulations, the individual crafts-

man had no freedom. Every invention which transcended the limited sphere of the craft was combatted and regarded with distrust as presenting a danger to the traditional basis of guild operations. . . ." Hence better design came not from stove builders but from laymen.

There was concern over the price of firewood toward the end of the eighteenth century in what is now Germany. There was concern over the vast quantities of wood then required to warm public buildings. One royal building inspec-

Figure 137 Long ago a visitor to the tile-stove regions of central Europe remarked that people there tended to warm themselves "very freely" before their stoves. This illustration, showing the stove on a horse blanket, dates from 1510.

Figure 138 This woodcut by Heinrich Aldegrever, done in 1532, shows Jacob contemplating Joseph's dreams. In the background is a three-tier tile stove. Tiles like the tall ones on the lower tier were often used for portraits. In Gdansk in Poland a tile stove thirty-nine feet high was built entirely of portrait tiles, most of them showing royalty.

tor worked for twenty years at that period attempting to improve stove efficiency, and according to Faber with considerable success—up to an 80 percent saving in wood. All of this activity sug-

gests a concern with fuel supply paralleling that in Sweden at the same period. It may or may not have meant an actual shortage of wood, something future doctoral theses may tell us. But the concern surely reflected a real pinch of some kind, related either to the availability or to the cost of fuel.

MODERN TILE STOVES

If design improvements in central European stoves were slow, they were nevertheless in time very effective. Today's tile stoves may have their equals for efficiency elsewhere; but I doubt that they are surpassed.

Figure 139 This woodcut made by Barthel Beham in the sixteenth century is titled "The Spinning Room"; a lot besides spinning seems to be going on. Tile stove at right. Foreign visitors long ago remarked on the great popularity of rooms warmed by such stoves in Germany; this woodcut suggests they were correct.

Figure 140 This domed clay stove from Germany has a bench around it for sitting or sleeping, and drying racks above for hanging clothes.

At present three basic types of central European tile stoves exist:

• The traditional wood-burning model designed to warm a room or two. These are medium to heavyweight models, storing much heat. Cooking and baking facilities may be built into some of these, as in Switzerland.

• Tile stoves of light-weight construction with warm-air heat. This system uses a cast-iron firebox within the tile stove structure. (See figures 161, 162.) It stores less heat. Room air circulates in a space between the iron firebox and the tile stove wall, warming by convection. Ducts may carry warm air to other rooms. The fire chamber may have a grate for coal or coke; it may be designed for wood; it may use oil or gas and there are electric models.

• Tile-stove central heat. This generally refers to a stove with hot water heating capacity, a boiler. Warm water is pumped through a radiator system to heat the entire house. The system can be tied in easily with existing oil or gas hot water heating systems. Fuels include the full range as with warm-air heat.

Figure 141 The woodwork built around this Swiss stove suggests how safe masonry stoves can be when properly constructed. This one is in the Engadiner Museum, St. Moritz.

Figure 142 A Swiss tile stove.

Figure 143 Tile stove with bench and sleeping platform. The stove was photographed in 1942 in the Slovenian region of Yugoslavia, formerly a part of Austria. Photo by Erika Groth-Schmachtenberger.

The adaptability of these systems to different fuels is no accident. As one German told me, "We have been through two wars. We know the value of a heating system that can be used with various fuels."

Two other distinctions are made by central Europeans: Their stoves are either for continuous firing or for intermittent firing.

Intermittent firing is for the traditional wood burning tile stove. It is fired once or twice a day, the firing lasting two to four hours. Heat storage capacity is large to bridge the time span between firings.

Continuous combustion is for the warm-air or boiler system. Usually it involves a cast-iron firebox using coal, coke, or wood. These stoves have less heat-storage capacity than traditional models, but far more than an iron or steel stove.

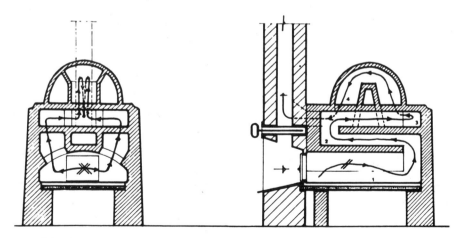

Figure 144 The horizontal firebox in this old-style Austrian stove is not recommended by designers today. The dome top, however, remains popular.

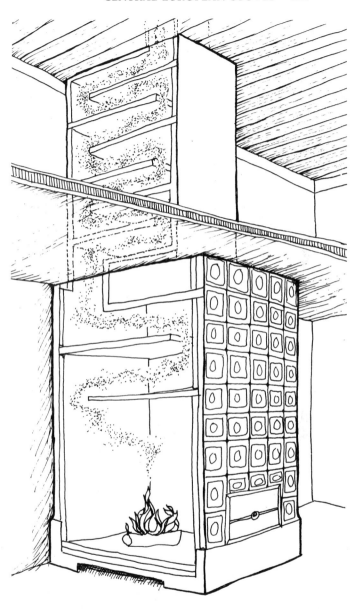

Figure 145 Two-story Austrian style stove, with tile surface on the first floor, plastered masonry above. Designed and built in the U.S. by Gustav Jung of Vienna.

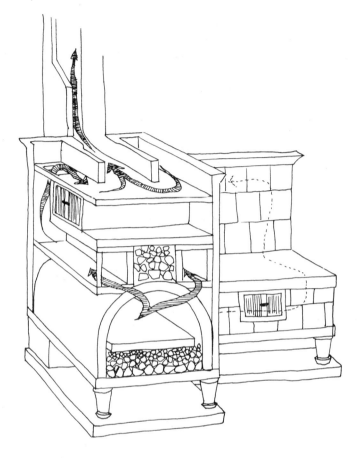

Figure 146 Typical Swiss combination oven and heating stove. The oven (lower level) is also the firebox. There is a warming oven as well on the next-to-the-top level, door at left. A tile-surfaced bench, with flues inside to warm it, is often built next to such an oven. A kitchen range, situated in an adjoining room, might supply heat to the bench; the oven is fired separately. Today hot water heating capacity may be built into stoves of this kind in Switzerland. The hot water is circulated to radiators in adjoining rooms, turning the oven into a central heater.

Stove Type	Heat Output in Kilocalories per Square Meter per Hour: Kcal/m²/hr.	Average Surface Temperature in °C (°F)
Iron or Steel	2,000–2,400	200–400°C (392–752°F)
Tile Stove continuous combustion	800–1,000	120–200°C (248–392°F)
Tile Stove traditional, intermittent firing	500–600	50–120°C (122–248°F)

Adapted from *Wood Burning* by Hans Winkelmann, director of the Central Swiss Forestry Office; United Nations (FAO) Rome, 1955.

Design differences between the two types lead to performance differences, as reflected in the table above.

Central Europe's tile stove builders sacrifice something, as the table shows, in adapting to the modern world. The surface temperature of continuous combustion models rises above the level some traditional stove builders consider reasonable for a healthy environment. Central European builders to whom I've spoken generally share the opinion that the lower surface temperature is best, both for comfort and health. But the twentieth century market called for more powerful heaters to warm the whole house. To compete with modern furnace technology tile-stove builders had to keep size and costs down, and they had to produce more heat. The result was compromise, something between a traditional masonry stove and an iron stove. The purists remain reluctant; they know the virtues and the value of the old system. But compromise kept the craft alive while in Sweden it has almost died out.

The compromise systems may appeal to many Americans reluctant to abandon central heating. The warm-air model is really a hybrid, combining iron and masory stoves in one. The cast-iron firebox is lined with brick to improve combustion. Heat transfer to the room is more rapid with the iron firebox than in the traditional stove. So the system responds more quickly to warm a cold room. Transfer of substantial heat from the firebox to the room also makes it possible to reduce or eliminate the masonry smoke channels within the stove. This simplifies construction and reduces costs.

To what degree transfer of heat from these iron fireboxes might reduce combustion efficiency and promote air pollution I can't say. So far as I'm aware no tests have been made. Many such fireboxes are used with coke or coal. I used a very large one with wood in the winter of 1981-1982 and can report that it developed an eight-foot flame path with no visible smoke coming from the chimney after start-up, a good sign as regards pollution. There was also prodigious heat production, and I've contemplated naming the thing Smaug after Tolkein's dragon. To me, the performance seemed impressive.

The advantages of iron-firebox and central-heat models, then, include:

• Quick response.

• Simpler construction and sharply reduced vulnerability to stress cracking.

• High heat output and the possibility of moving heat to other rooms.

• Ability to burn a variety of fuels.

Possible disadvantages would include a reduced heat-storage capacity (though this can become an advantage in mild weather) and higher stove-surface temperatures. Iron-firebox models have been very popular in Germany and Austria. About 90 percent of German masonry stoves built today use iron fireboxes.

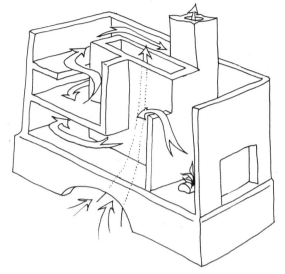

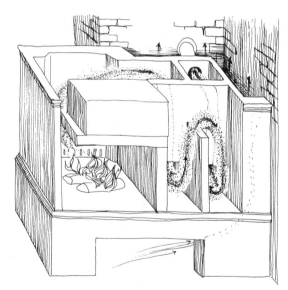

Figure 147 Austrian tile stove, after a design by Josef Thurner. Note passage for room air, which enters beneath stove and emerges between stove and wall. This technique preserves the side of the stove adjacent to the wall as a radiating surface.

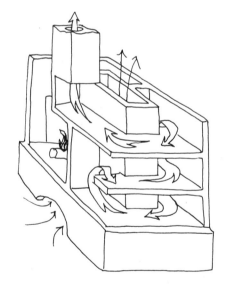

Figures 148 and 149 Two views of a rather complex Austrian stove designed by Josef Thurner. Note shaft at center of stove, through which room air passes, increasing radiating surface.

Chapter
11

Choosing
A Heat Storage
Stove

asonry heating systems are a new idea in North America. At the moment few can build or design them. But this is changing. Interest has begun to grow rapidly and possibilities are expanding. For example:

- One U.S. company has begun mass producing components for a heat-storage fireplace (see figure 163). The same company has a masonry stove in test stages at present; core components of the stove are made of refractory concrete on a concrete block machine. Early testing suggests clean combustion and very high efficiency. Mass production should mean prices within the budgets of many homeowners.

- Austrian, Swedish, and German tile stoves have become available in the U.S. They are likely to be outstanding in efficiency and appearance. The price is high because materials (and sometimes the stove builder) must be imported. But quality is likely to be very high as well.

- Iron fireboxes for masonry stoves are becoming available here and there in North America. They seem likely to become much more widely available as interest in masonry stoves increases, for reasons outlined later in this chapter.

- In New England, especially, a brick stove vogue has begun to develop and spread. The brick models are often described as Russian stoves or Russian fireplaces. The latter generally have large double doors so that the fire can be seen. Some of these stoves do indeed follow east European peasant designs, although not necessarily Russian ones. Their owners generally seem quite pleased with them. A few of these stoves have failed, through poor or amateurish design and workmanship, but that's to be expected occasionally with a new product.

- A few builders have begun experimenting with the very intriguing possibility of combining masonry stoves and fireplace stoves with solar heating systems.

- A few importers are bringing in small, portable tile stoves from Europe. These are manufactured whereas the traditional masonry stove is built in place and is too massive to move.

In coming years, masonry stove design techniques will become more widely known. But it's possible now to set some guidelines for judging what's available and what's likely to become available in the future.

MASONRY STOVES AND SOLAR HEAT

Students of solar heating divide their systems into two classes, passive and active. The active systems are mechanically more complex. They involve more or less elaborate heat collectors, pumps, blowers, controls—manufactured components. These can cost a lot of money and they can get out of whack. This has discouraged some from the idea of solar heat.

Passive solar heating is simpler. Stone Age man knew about it. So did Aristotle. For passive solar heating you let the sun into the house and then try to trap and store its warmth. You let that warmth circulate in the building by natural air movement. That's all there is to it. Passive systems built in recent years can fill a major part of the dwelling's heating needs, even in severe climates. They do so at reasonable cost and there is little or nothing to break down. But cold nights and cloudy days do require a backup heating system.

All passive systems need some way to store solar heat for use in sunless periods. Water tanks, rock piles, and masonry walls and floors have become the common means of storage. The materials are low in cost and readily available. These same materials can also be used to store heat from a wood fire, doubling the usefulness of a solar storage system. The masonry stove becomes an ideal backup for solar heating.

Figures 150 through 152 show typical storage arrangements for passive solar heating systems. To adapt them to wood heat, stoves or flues would be built into the storage mass.

Experiments in solar heating have become common; so have experiments in wood heat. But very little has been done toward combining wood and solar heat storage systems. Shortly after World War II, there was a flurry of interest in solar heating that came to an end as cheap oil and gas swept the heating market. But before they did, several American architects experimented with systems that suggest patterns for today.

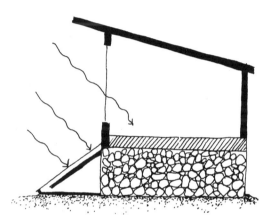

Figure 150 Solar collector plus rock storage under floor.

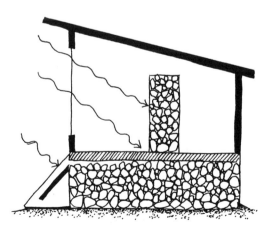

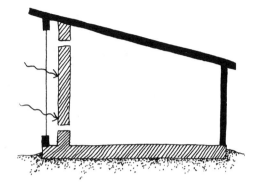

Figure 152 Trombe wall.

Two such architects, Alden and Peggy Krider of Manhattan, Kansas, built for their own use two solar houses with ducted hot-air heating systems installed under a masonry floor. Both were really modern adaptations of radiant floor heating systems first used long ago in the Far East and in the Roman Empire. The second house, which the Kriders occupy today, was built in 1952. It is oriented so that the sun pours in the southern windows, striking the stone walls and floor that provide a large storage mass for the sun's heat. Ducts beneath the floor carry warmth from a gas furnace; but the furnace could just as well have been wood-fired, as in ancient Rome.

Like other users of radiant floor systems, the Kriders have found theirs very comfortable. Air temperatures are uniform from floor to ceiling, drafts at a minimum. A Kansas City architect, I. Lloyd Roark, built a subfloor duct system out of hollow tiles at the same period. "I liked the system very well," he told me in a letter. "The floors are beauti-

ful, the cost of operation phenomenally low in a tough climate, and the natural humidity and air-blown dust control inherent in all radiant systems a real joy." Roark found construction problems in using relatively small hollow tiles (five by twelve by twelve inches). But these should be minimized by using larger precast duct systems, or a plenum similar to that used by the Kriders.

Figures 153 and 154 show duct layout systems for two hypocaustlike heating

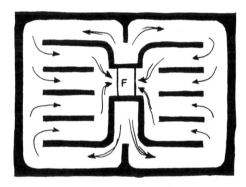

Figure 153 Parallel duct layout for Alden Krider's floor-heating system.

Figure 154 Serpentine duct layout for the Krider floor-heating system.

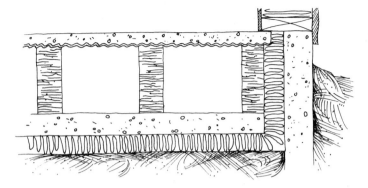

Figure 155   Floor detail for Krider system. See text for construction details.

systems designed by Alden Krider. The ducts are formed by placing four-by-eight-by-sixteen-inch concrete blocks on edge on a two-inch concrete slab. The blocks are lined up on twenty-four-inch centers. Corrugated sheet metal rests on top of the block piers (see figure 155), and a one-and-one-half-inch concrete floor slab rests on top of this. The relatively thin floor slab offers a quicker heating response than the heavy slabs of Roman times, which were six or more inches thick. Insulation around the perimeter of the duct system is essential. The need for insulation beneath the floor depends on soil conditions, Prof. Krider believes. He recommends insulation where soil conditions are moist, because moisture will increase heat loss into the earth. With dry or rocky soil, he feels that insulation is less necessary; the subsoil may then prove useful as an added heat sink. Prof. Krider suggests the parallel duct layout (above) for larger instal-

lations, and the serpentine layout for smaller ones.

Don Metz is one of the leading architects in underground housing design. At his home in Lyme, New Hampshire, he has installed a hot-air system to supply heat beneath a concrete slab floor with a tile surface. The floor slab rests on concrete block piers seated on another slab eight inches below, thus creating an open air space, or plenum, for air circulation. A wood-burning furnace supplies the hot air, the furnace being set in a long basement room running the length of the house beneath its center. This room also serves for wood storage. Because the house is dug into a hillside, one end of the room opens at ground level on the south side. This makes for easy access when it is time to get the wood in, an important consideration in the design of any building dependent on wood heat.

When he built the system, Metz hoped that natural convection would be enough to pull warm air out of the basement, the warm air passing through registers along the outer walls into the space above. "No dice," he said. "Ninety degrees in the basement, sixty degrees up above. I then decided to pump air into the plenum. That works very well. The upper slab is a perfectly located thermal storage mass, warmish to the naked foot.

Experimenters at the University of Florida conducted tests over a three-year period on a house with an under-floor plenum. They concluded that radiant floor heat improves comfort to such a degree that occupants will set thermostats lower. A thermostat set lower by three degrees, they estimated, would cut fuel costs by 10 percent.

Other conclusions reached by the Florida study:

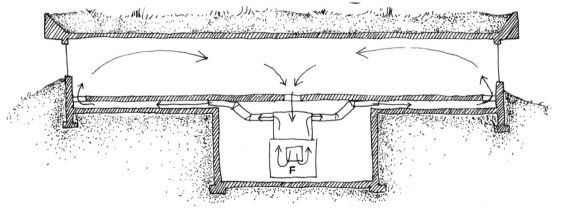

Figure 156   Subfloor heating system in Metz house. *F* indicates furnace, from which hot air is blown into under-floor plenum.

- Warm air was well diffused even in rooms with high (cathedral) ceilings. There was minimal stratification; air temperatures near the floor and ceiling differed by only a couple of degrees.

- Air flowed evenly from the registers to all parts of the house.

- Air pressure in the plenum and in the living space tended to be the same, so that the blower was essential (as Metz found) to send warmth up from plenum to living area.

- The deeper the plenum, the more warm air was required to fill and warm it. But plenum depth does not affect efficiency as long as the foundation walls are well insulated.

Prof. Richard C. Hill of the University of Maine has built two of the most interesting experimental wood burners of recent years. One of these provides backup heat for a solar system at the Maine Audubon Society headquarters in Falmouth. To maintain the high temperatures necessary for good combustion, the firebox was built to contain heat rather than transmit it. The firebox is so well insulated, in fact, that its outer walls are close to room temperature even when internal temperatures approach 2,000°F. To transfer to the building the heat generated in this furnace, Prof. Hill used a king-sized stovepipe, one hundred sixty feet of eight-inch galvanized culvert. The cul-

vert carries furnace heat to a rock bed containing 105 tons of one-inch stone that also stores heat from the solar collector. This transfer system is so effective that gases leaving the furnace at 2,000°F cool to 120°F by the time they leave the chimney. The culvert is, in fact, too long for natural draft; the draft must be induced by a fan in the chimney.

After using if for a year, the Audubon Society reported that its furnace was the single most successful element in their heating system. The furnace used only four and a half cords of wood to supplement solar heat in a 5,500-square-foot building. That was during the severe winter of 1977. Houses less than half the size often use twice as much wood in a similar climate.

The firebox in Prof. Hill's Audubon furnace is lined with four inches of castable refractory material. Next comes a brick wall, then four inches of perlite insulation, a second brick wall, a four-inch air space, then a third brick wall, which forms the outer surface of the furnace. All this is designed to contain heat and keep combustion temperatures high. A fan blows air into the firebox under pressure. This, in combination with the Venturi passage, creates turbulence in the firebox and good mixing of fuel and air. Turbulence acts to remove ash cover from the wood, improving exposure to oxygen. Another fan in the chimney helps to draw hot gases through one hundred sixty feet of steel culvert, where they lose their heat to the rock bed.

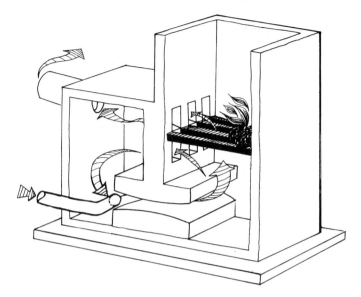

Figure 157 Prof. Richard C. Hill's Maine Audubon furnace. Combustion air is blown in at lower left, then passes through a Venturi into firebox. Leaving the firebox, some gases again pass through the Venturi; the rest move out to rock storage bed through duct at upper left.

Although it worked well, Prof. Hill remained unsatisfied with the Audubon furnace. He felt the rock-bed storage system was too massive and slow to warm. He was also concerned about a tendency for flames to shoot out the fuel door when it was opened. He also wanted to design a safe and effective smaller furnace for household use, one usable even in urban areas where pollution problems are acute. A large influx of inefficient (and thus smoky) stoves has already begun to create serious pollution in some communities.

Prof. Hill's second furnace is a boiler. That is, it uses wood to heat water, and the water (rather than a rock bed) stores the heat generated. The hot water can then be pumped through radiators to warm the house. The whole thing could of course be tied in with a solar hot water heating system. Prof. Hill has built several versions of the new furnace under a Department of Energy grant. Efficiency may run as high as 80 percent. There are no chimney deposits, which means good, clean combustion. A 500-gallon water storage tank will store 500,000 Btu, and the system can provide domestic hot water as well. One particular advantage of the Hill furnace is that, unlike the typical wood stove, it seems able to use a half-and-half mix of dry and green wood without a creosote penalty. Presumably it would burn pine or other softwoods with equal lack of difficulty.

One of the difficulties in any wood-burning boiler is the tendency of the water jacket to cool the firebox and retard combustion. Prof. Hill's boiler solves this problem with an unusual firebox. The firebox itself is an insulated refractory chamber where high temperatures can build without interference from the cooling waters. The fuel sits in a steel cylinder surrounded by a water jacket. Only the lower end of the wood in the cylinder burns, the portion extending down into the refractory chamber. As this lower end burns, the log drops steadily into the chamber. A refractory channel just beyond the fire chamber reaches red heat, and gases cooked out of the wood burn as they pass through it. Leaving the refractory channel, the gases carry their heat up through another water-jacketed steel cylinder, which is the heat exchanger. Here the gases give up their heat to the water, which then circulates into the storage tank. The burning rate is very steady; a forty-pound load of wood burns to ashes in about two hours, aided by forced draft and a chimney exhaust fan. Once the walls of the refractory chamber reach red heat, even a single unsplit log will burn in the furnace. Prof. Hill estimated that the furnace would be fired once a day in mild weather and up to four times a day during the cold part of a Maine winter. The heat stored in the tank is released as the house requires it. The base of the furnace, containing the refractory chambers, is insulated with several inches of vermiculite cement.

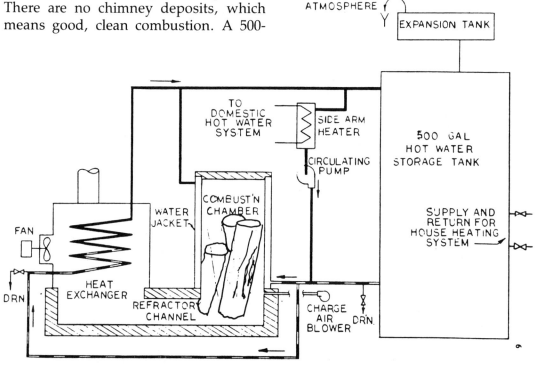

Figure 158 Schematic drawing of Hill boiler. The upper part of the combustion chamber is a steel cylinder with a water jacket. The lower part is made of castable refractory, as is the channel beyond to the left. The whole combustion area—chamber, channel, and the area just below the heat exchanger—is encased in a mix of eight parts vermiculite to one and one-half parts Portland cement, to a depth of several inches. The vermiculite concrete, a good insulator, is coated with block bond to give it durability.

Even after two hours' firing at high temperature, the outer surface remains cool to the touch.

Dumont Industries (Monmouth, ME 04259) manufactures a version of the Hill boiler called the Tempest. This is a furnace rather than a masonry stove in the normal sense of the term. But I have included it here because the Hill boiler operates on masonry stove principles, providing heat storage and using high temperature combustion in a refractory chamber.

BRICK STOVES

A virtue of the brick stove is that it can be built by an American mason with a minimum of special training. Materials are available, so they do not have to be imported. The result, even with quite primitive designs, can be very pleasing. Shape is flexible. Surfaces may be plastered or inset with decorative tiles. Built-in niches can hold candlesticks. Many attractive designs are possible.

Often brick models are described as Russian stoves or fireplaces. Some brick stoves now being built in the U.S. follow patterns used in east Europe, Finland, the east Baltic area, and Russia. Some follow American designs devised by amateur builders and labeled Russian, perhaps because of virtues thought to be associated with the name. None of the models I've heard about or seen follows the pattern of the traditional Russian stove, familiar from Tolstoy. Nor, for the

most part, do they follow the patterns of more modern Russian stoves like those shown in the appendix. So let us forget the "Russian" stove, and talk about masonry stoves as built in the U.S.

To begin with, it is probably worthwhile to unravel the story of how the current brick stove vogue began in the U.S. In 1976, the late Jaan Jaakson aroused interest with an article in *Wood Burning Quarterly*. Jaakson described stove-building techniques from his native Estonia, and offered to teach others his methods. Unfortunately, he died in an automobile accident before he could do so.

Jaakson's article contained drawings of two brick stoves that he labeled early and primitive designs (figures 104 and 105). Both had been used not only in Estonia but also in the east Baltic area generally and in Russia. In southern Maine a carpenter named Basilio Lepuschenko has for twenty years or so been building stoves much like the Jaakson model shown in figure 105. The Lepuschenko stoves have either three or five up-and-down smoke channels above the firebox, and they have been built mainly for members of the émigré Russian community around Richmond, Maine.

In recent years, with interest created by the oil crisis after 1973, Lepuschenko began teaching his methods to others and selling plans for his stove. Albie Barden, a stove dealer in Norridgewok, Maine, spread the plans through magazine articles and a newsletter. He formed the Masonry Stove Builders Guild and

Figure 159 Brick stove of a type pioneered in Maine by Basilio Lepuschenko, based on old east European designs. A good many stoves of this type have been built in the northeastern U.S. Typically, the vertical smoke channels are each eight by twelve inches and not more than forty-eight inches in height. The firebox is about a foot wide, sixteen inches high, and thirty inches or more in length. The chimney flue would be a standard eight-by-eight inch model. Detailed plans are available from Mr. Lepuschenko. See Information Sources at the back of the book.

began holding workshops, both to experiment with brick-stove construction and to help others learn the techniques. Many if not most of the masons building brick stoves today learned their technique through Albie Barden's workshops. (See Appendix 2, Information Sources.)

Early brick stoves in Maine were often based on Lepuschenko models. Essentially these are peasant stoves. They suffer from what most European stove builders would call poor firebox design. The long, low firebox provides a poor atmosphere for combustion; so do the heavy logs such a firebox may tend to invite. In his article Jaan Jaakson illustrated an improved version of this sort of stove (figure 106), in which the firebox was made shorter and higher in relation to length.

More recently Albie Barden and his associates have been working with a more sophisticated design they call the contraflow or fountain. The name comes from the way the gases flow in this tall stove. They rise from the firebox to the top of the stove through a central channel, then flow downward through two broad channels, which bring heat in contact with the outer walls of the stove. At the same time convection air rises along the stove's outer wall. This is an old design. A Swedish engineer seems to have invented it, but the Finns and the Russians have given it the widest use. (See figures 179 and 183 in the appendix.)

In Finland today, government tax policy encourages masonry stoves. The Finnish architect Heikki Hyytiainen has been at work trying to improve contraflow and other designs in recent years in his own country. Barden has studied these designs abroad, and introduced them in the U.S. Both he and Hyytiainen are working on books that should in time make further details on the Finnish methods available.

A capable masonry stove designer plans very carefully the movement of hot gases through the stove. The goal—impossible but to be approached—is an even surface temperature without hot spots. Hot spots create stress in the masonry and contribute to cracking. The cracks that appear may be tiny, barely visible except to the practiced eye, and without structural importance. Still they represent a design failure and are to be avoided. In stoves with full-closure dampers, the cracks are a potential safety hazard.

Now of course it isn't possible to achieve perfectly even heat distribution over the stove's surface. So where there are potential hot spots, the builder *designs* for stress—he builds to allow and to compensate for extra heat. Remember that with the Korean ondol, the floor was made thickest where the heat of the stove first struck it. In a brick or tile stove, the wall may in the same way be thickened to accommodate stress.

A stove like the Lepuschenko model, for example (figure 159) take the hot blast from the firebox along the back wall, opposite the fuel door. In the first model of this kind that I saw, there were fine stress cracks through the wall at the mortar joints. One way to compensate for this would be to make the wall two bricks thick instead of one, providing more masonry to absorb the heat and reducing stress. A mason who has tried this method told me that it eliminated cracking problems in the back wall of the stove.

Now back to the question of those hairline stress cracks, and the reason they concern me. Virtually all brick stoves built in the U.S. now use a chimney damper. This is a sliding damper that you are expected to close completely after the fire burns down to coals. Swedish, Russian, Finnish, and east European stoves generally operate in this same way. (See chapters 9 and 13 for more details.) You must have a complete-closure damper in such stoves for two reasons: The tiny stress cracks will admit air to the stove, and so will the doors unless they are airtight. Without a damper that blocks the chimney flue completely, air moves through the stove and carries heat up the chimney. Efficiency drops. The closed damper compensates for the fact that the fuel door and the stove wall are not airtight. If you have observed how air drawn through a brick chimney wall can feed a fire in the flue, you will appreciate just how much air can move into a stove in this way, and how much heat can be lost without a full-closure damper. The trouble is, closing such a damper prematurely may force lethal gases into the house through leaky stove doors or walls. These gases, which may include carbon monoxide, can cause headaches or even asphyxiation. I stress the risk because I believe the full-closure damper is a most unwise device. It would be risky on any sort of stove or furnace; note that the dampers for stove-pipe used with iron stoves block only about 80 percent of the pipe. And full closure is unnecessary for efficiency, if certain other steps be taken. For example:

- Airtight fuel and ash doors can quite effectively block most air movement into the stove around these doors. (I doubt that any "airtight" stove is wholly airtight.)

- The Swiss have shown that a coat of plaster blocks 96 percent of air movement through a chimney wall. It should do as much for stove walls.

- If added precautions are needed, use a damper in the central European mode that closes only 80 percent of the way. This is far less risky than the full-closure model.

A brick stove wall is commonly one brick thick. When a stress crack opens between bricks, it runs right through from inside to outside. One of the great advantages of the tile stove wall is that it is *three* layers thick. The layers may not add up in thickness to one four-inch American brick. But two of the layers overlap. No joint runs through from outside to inside the stove, and air movement through such a wall is much less likely. A second plaster layer would pro-

vide a similar safety factor for the brick stove. The ingenious will find various other ways of making the stove wall tight; the important thing is that it be done.

Brick stoves, of course, are not limited in style to those currently being built in the U.S. Virtually any of the tile stove models shown in this book could also be built of brick. The elegant designs of Cronstedt and Wrede in Sweden were intended originally to be built of either tile or brick. Tile models found their way into the homes of the well-to-do; brick stoves appeared in Swedish farmhouses, where they were often plastered and whitewashed. Special high-temperature paints have also been used to coat brick stoves, and also sheet metal.

Tile stove builders in central Europe believe strongly that their product is superior to the brick stove. They feel the tile wall is structurally superior, that the stove is more responsive, and that it generally performs better. Gustav Jung of Vienna is a rare craftsman who has built and used east European brick stoves, including contraflow models, as well as the tile stoves of his native Austria. With a lifetime of experience in stove building, he is an unequivocal believer in the tile stove and in central European design. The brick contraflow model, he feels, does not compare. People in east Europe and Finland, on the other hand, are quite happy with their brick stoves, and the efficiency figures they produce suggest that, in this respect at least, the brick stoves are in no way inferior to tile models. In time, if comparative testing

can be undertaken, we may have definitive answers to such questions. Meantime there is something else worth noting here. The central European climate is milder than that of Finland or northern Russia; light- to medium-weight stove walls are appropriate. The thick stove wall may be more appropriate for heavier heating requirements in Finland, Russia, or the northern U.S. Another point noted earlier but worth repeating: The heavier the wall and the more massive the stove, the more readily it withstands the stress that must come from a large heat output. There is more mass to absorb the heat and so reduce expansion/contraction.

Central Europeans have made one innovation in brick stoves that makes sense to me. They use wire ties between bricks, just as they do in tile stoves, to pull the structure together and resist expansion stress.

IMPORTED TILE STOVES

European tile stoves of two types are available in the U.S. First there are the large tile stoves built in place with imported materials, often by a European stove builder. These are identical with the traditional tile stoves of central and north Europe. Few have been built here, in part because the stoves are unfamiliar to Americans, and in part because costs are high. Importing materials *and* a masonry specialist is expensive. One two-story Austrian stove built in Littleton, New Hampshire, cost about $15,000. It

Figure 160 Contemporary Austrian stove. The tile is green.

was built for the White Mountain School by Gustav Jung and his son, Gunther, Viennese master stove builders. The stove is of course much larger than would be normal for a dwelling; it heats a school building. But it does suggest why imported tile stoves, handsome and effective as they may be, are unlikely to become a mass-market item here immediately. If tiles and masons with the skills to use them become readily available, the situation could change. There is currently a one-year waiting period for construction of tile stoves in Austria. Stoves so popular there seem likely to be equally popular here, once they are understood and their virtues appreciated.

A second imported model is the portable manufactured tile stove. These may have complex interior flues. They may be quite efficient. In effect they are an attempt to provide tile-stove style and appearance in a small package. But a major virtue of the tile or brick stove, its heat-storage capacity, just does not fit into a small package. The portable stoves thus have to be burned on a continuous basis (with coal or wood fuel) to provide heat. In operation they are more like iron stoves than like true heat-storage stoves. If you like the appearance, and can pay the price, they are handsome and probably efficient stoves. Don't depend on them to add significant heat storage to your home.

IRON/MASONRY COMBINATION SYSTEMS

If you want a heat-storage stove but can't afford imported tile, or if you can't find a competent stove mason, there are other possibilities.

Recently I built well-insulated living quarters in one end of an old cow barn. A section of the floor thirty feet by seventeen is brick, and the sun pours in upon this through a half dozen casement windows. Under the brick lies six inches of sand and under that two inches of insulation atop a rock bed. While waiting to install a masonry heater, I hooked up a small cast-iron cookstove. Its peak efficiency is probably about 50 percent; very likely it was no more than 40 percent the way I ran it.

The first year, with vital portions of overhead insulation not in place, I heated 1,200 square feet of living space on three and a half cords of wood. The winter was cold and there were no insulating shutters on the glass. For various reasons, I used the stove as one would a masonry model, firing it fast and hot for short periods. Probably I fired it four hours a day on the average. A *lot* of heat went up the chimney; the rest soaked into the brick floor and the sand below it. I found that if I fired from 7 to 9 in the evening, the bricks would remain comfortable to walk upon barefoot the next morning. And this in January. Now it is November and one firing a day is enough in the morning if it is cloudy; I need no fire at all in sunny weather, though the outdoor temperature drops to 25°F at night.

Now this is a very crude way to heat masonry, not efficient at all. But efficiency was not the idea. I wanted to test the effects of occasional bursts of heat in a heavily insulated structure with heat storage. The improvement in atmosphere was remarkable. I have lived for eight years with iron-stove heat. The stove ran twenty-four hours a day from late October to early April, by which time the interior of my nose felt like the nostril of a camel caught in a Sahara sandstorm. But running an iron stove for only four hours a day, and depending on heat stored from both sun and stove in the brick floor—that was an entirely different matter. The air felt soft and comfortable, rarely hot and dry. Time devoted to stove-tending dropped off dramatically. I found I could leave the place without heat for two or three days in the coldest weather; the temperature fell so slowly that I did not have to worry about bursting pipes. No doubt I could have left for longer periods. The experience has convinced me of one thing: In any future structure that I build, most heat will come from a low-level radiant source —a masonry stove, a warm floor or wall. Possibly the initial cost will be a bit higher. But the result is worth it; there is no comparison with any other form of heat.

I'm not even convinced that initial cost need be much higher. A little of the ingenuity of North American builders needs to be put to work here to design simple and effective masonry fireboxes. It is also possible to line the firebox of a cheap iron stove with firebrick to improve combustion. The iron stove can then be used to warm masonry: House the stove in a masonry shell, then run the flue through a rock bed or through a masonry room divider. Such a system may lack Baron Cronstedt's finesse in flue design, and it may not reach the pinnacle of efficiency. But my own experience is that it can be very satisfactory to live with. If a little care is taken in design and material selection, the system need not suffer in efficiency or durability, either.

Prof. Richard Hill's furnace built for the Maine Audubon Society is an ingenious design. But it is worth keeping in mind that it is not all that different in concept from what north Europeans

were doing with the steinofen one thousand years ago, or from what *Homo erectus* appears to have been doing three hundred thousand years before that: heating rocks. Do not be daunted by the complexity of some old designs. Some of these were elegant, and some worked admirably. But remember that all you are doing is heating bricks, or tiles, or rocks, or possibly water. Let your imagination roam a bit as you consider how this may be done with modern materials and techniques. But keep in mind:

- The need for a very hot fire chamber of suitable shape.

- The need for construction techniques and material suited to high temperatures.

- The need for adequate storage for heat generated—in rocks, brick, tile, or water. (Water requires special safety precautions; consult a boiler expert.)

- The need for adequate heat transfer. After you have generated the heat and stored it, make sure it gets transferred to the room instead of exiting up the chimney.

Iron fireboxes especially designed for use in masonry heating systems are widely available in central Europe. These fireboxes may not gain the approval of purists in masonry stove design, but I think they could find wide use in North America. The iron firebox simplifies construction. It raises heat output to levels

useful in the colder regions. It makes it possible to burn coal or coke in a masonry stove, and to move heat via ducts or pipes to other rooms.

The purist believes that an all-masonry design offers the closest thing to a

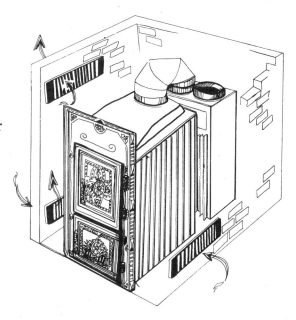

Figure 161 Masonry stoves using cast iron fireboxes have become very common in Germany and Austria. The enclosing masonry stores heat. But heat also reaches the room by convection, via grates in the masonry structure. The model above—with a heat exchanger behind the firebox—has been tested at 85 percent efficiency using wood fuel by the German standards institute (DIN). The distance between the masonry wall of the stove and the iron firebox is critical. It should be twelve to fifteen centimeters, or about five to six inches. A modified masonry smoke channel system can be used with these fireboxes, but today iron heat exchangers are more common.

Figure 162 Cast iron firebox for a masonry stove. The firebox is lined with firebrick. The lower door is for ash removal; the middle door is for fuel; the upper door is for the baking oven. The entire firebox can be slid out of the brickwork (some models even have wheels) to provide access to the masonry enclosure.

completely radiant form of heat, and he doesn't want to compromise that. He objects to the increased convection off the side of an iron firebox. He objects to the dust that such a firebox may fry. However, I've used a European iron firebox (brick-lined)—the aforementioned Smaug—in the quarters described earlier. I fired it as I did the cookstove, for only an hour or two at a time once or twice a day, using scraps from a wooden heel factory as fuel. I noticed that the results were far superior to those obtained from running an iron stove twenty-four hours a day. The purist has my sympathy; I believe in his theories. But I've found that there is a lot of satisfaction to be had from a compromise design, and at lower cost, which will be important to many.

Figure 163 Heat storage fireplaces are an old idea in Scandinavia. They deserve a modern rebirth, and Thermal Energy Storage Systems (TESS) of Kenvil, N.J. has taken a long step in this direction. The TESS fireplace is in the Rumford mode; it reflects heat back to the room just as a band shell reflects sound. But there is a difference. The core structure is made of concrete block specially shaped and designed for the purpose. The firebox and the block just above it are made of refractory concrete. After smoke leaves the firebox, it passes through eight narrow zig-zagging channels parallel to each other. Here heat is absorbed that would otherwise be lost up the chimney. Along both sides and the back of the fireplace, from the floor to ceiling level, passages are built into the block for circulation of room air. As the air moves through these passages, it picks up heat from the hot core of the unit and recirculates it to the room. The block core of the system can be laid up very quickly; the company has tried to design it so that the owner-builder can handle construction. The core is then enclosed with brick or other masonry, and glass doors enclose the fire area. Combustion air comes from outside the house via a duct in the hearth. A typical TESS fireplace with brick veneer would weigh about 13,300 pounds. If that mass of masonry is raised 100° degrees above room temperature, then the masonry will store 266,000 Btu. That's

At present, none of the European iron fireboxes is widely available in the U.S. Because of their general usefulness I believe they will become more readily available in the near future, possibly by the time this book is published. If so the sources listed in the back should have information.

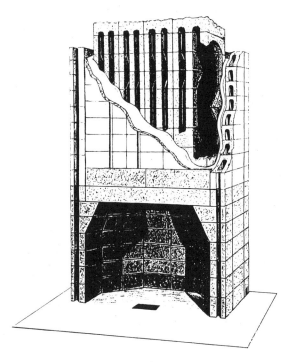

enough to keep most houses warm for several hours. Cost of the block core (currently $1,095 FOB Kenvil) should make the fireplace very competitive. The company has a high efficiency masonry stove in the testing stage and other products in design. Photo courtesy of Thermal Energy Storage Systems, Box M, Kenvil, N.J. 07847.

A PERSONAL NOTE ON HEAT AND HOUSES

It is important, as noted earlier, to consider the house as a functioning part of the heating system. The house is the larger chamber within which heat flows, or does not flow, to keep you warm. In writing about masonry stoves, and in making suggestions on their use, I have certain notions in mind as to what constitutes good house design. If the heating advice is to make sense, it is important to know what these ideas are. Briefly, I have assumed:

- That anyone building or remodeling today should take advantage of solar heat.

- That this be done via passive rather than active means.

- That the passive system would be modest in scale, comprising south-oriented windows rather than whole walls of glass.

- That the modest solar scale would be achieved by insulating heavily. That is, reduce heating requirements rather than increase the supply of heat.

- That the dwelling should combine means of storing both solar warmth and that of the backup heating system, whether fueled by wood, coal, or whatever.

In the rush to meet new energy needs since 1973, there has been a natural tendency among enthusiasts to cry: "Solar is the answer!" Lately the cry has gone up for envelope houses and superinsulated houses, which William Shurcliff has discussed so well. My own belief is that it is time for some sort of balance to be struck. Insulation has its virtues. So do solar and wood heat. But a house is a complex structure, serving many different ends; single-minded "solutions" tend to run into difficulty. For example:

- The wall-of-glass approach to solar leads to difficulty in preventing heat loss at night. It may lead to inordinate heat buildup at the wrong time. Glass walls are fragile and expensive.

- Superinsulation can provide a building so tight and energy efficient that it does not require a furnace. Human beings, a herd of gerbils, or candles will keep it warm most or all of the time. But a problem then develops in getting enough air into the place to avoid indoor pollution. The solution now proposed is an air-to-air heat exchanger, which runs on electricity. This device pumps fresh air in and old air out after extracting the heat.

- Very tight and well-insulated passive solar houses quite often run into problems of moisture buildup. That can be handled, of course; one way would be to plug in a dehumidifier.

Now I don't mean to imply that such problems are objections to solar heating, or to heavy insulation. Quite the opposite. What I am suggesting is more balance in the system: south windows that let in a good bit of sun but do not leave one in an expensive goldfish bowl. I want plenty of insulation but not the airless tomb effect. I do not want to be dependent on electricity to move air into and out of the house, or to dehumidify the place.

I am not prejudiced against electricity, but power in my area fails several times each winter. If I were dependent on it for fresh air or heat, I would be out of luck, sometimes for days. To me one of the main reasons to have solar heat or wood heat is that it lets me, in some small way, function more independently. Then when the power failure occurs, I can still cope. The water arrives by gravity feed. The heat comes from sun and wood. I have no problem with indoor pollution or moisture buildup because the fire, that engine of air movement, dries the place out a bit and keeps fresh air moving through. My goal is to use a modest amount of wood each winter—say one to three cords, an amount I could cut without a chain saw if necessary—and let the house breathe. I might have insulated so that a candle and three cats kept the place warm. But I am glad to have a fire, and to know that it is winter. Ideally, I believe the right way to heat such a dwelling is with the sun plus a masonry stove: safe, efficient, attractive, comfortable to live with, and not terribly demanding to operate.

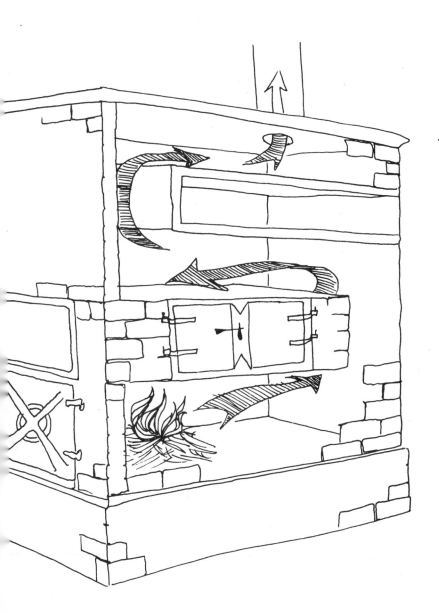

Chapter
12

Wood-burning
Fundamentals

Over the years I have learned that there are many misconceptions about wood burning. Some are perpetuated in books. Others fall into the realm of folklore. For example:

- There are people who pay $85 a cord for hardwood when they could buy softwood for little or nothing. But they believe pine, spruce, and hemlock are worthless fuels and that burning them will clog the chimney with soot.

- Others burn wood through a lifetime, suffering periodic chimney fires and the risk of losing their homes. They believe that chimney fires are an inevitable part of wood burning.

Figure 164 Children gathering wood fuel in the Yemen Arab Republic, 1972. FAO photo by F. Mattioli.

136

Many people have installed their own stoves under the impression they got sound advice on this from a neighbor or dealer. Perhaps they did. But there is a fire chief with a dry sense of humor over in Vermont, where more than half the people burn wood, who said, "A safe stove installation is hard to find. I understand there's one over near Montpelier." Experience suggests that he exaggerates only a little. A very little.

The following, then, is intended for experienced wood burners as well as neophytes. Wood burning can be safe, efficient and clean. All that's necessary is that a little attention be paid.

It is useful to think of fire as an engine for moving air within a building. Air warmed in a firebox becomes buoyant, expands, rises up the chimney. Cooler air flows in to replace it and the process feeds upon itself: air flows steadily into the building, into the stove, up and out the chimney. Fire is the engine of movement, warming air so that it flows upward.

Now this upward flow can be rapid and of large volume, as it would be with a fireplace. Then a lot of heat will flow outdoors. But you don't want that. For efficiency you want just enough air to flow into the stove to support good combustion *and* to keep the flow moving, to keep updraft alive in the chimney. As the stove's operator, you regulate air flow into the firebox; you minimize that flow or you enlarge it. Thus you become a major influence on the stove's efficiency. The best-designed stoves may suffer from unskilled operation.

Stand back now and look at the components of the wood-burning system: the house itself, the stove, the stovepipe, the chimney, the fuel and the person feeding it to the stove. Whether the whole system works well or poorly depends a lot on how well matched these components are. Virtually all emphasis today is placed on the stove. When something goes wrong, the tendency is to blame its design. There may indeed be faults in the design, but other factors are more common sources of trouble:

- Lack of skill in the stove's operator.

- Leaky houses, difficult to heat.

- Stoves poorly matched to house or climate, or poorly located within the building.

- Chimneys poorly designed for use with any stove, or poorly matched in size to the stove attached.

Many stoves operate at low efficiency (50 to 55 percent). Some are unsafe. But most of them work. Serious *operational* problems developing from the design of the stove itself are uncommon. So begin by thinking of the stove as part of a system, not as an object that stands or falls by itself. The system, to work well, must have well-matched components. Remember that you are one of them.

HEAT

In *The Meaning of the Twentieth Century*, Kenneth Boulding remarks that "There is therefore a kind of thermodynamic dismal theorem which sees the end of the universe as a uniform soup. . . . All things will be at the same temperature . . . nothing more can happen." Warm things tend to dissipate heat. They seek the temperature of their surroundings. This is true of coffee. It is true of houses. It is true of people, rabbits, stoves, and the planet. Everything seeks the temperature of the surrounding soup.

But life resists the trend. You feed the body to keep the inner fire going. You feed the stove to maintain warm surroundings. You build a house to shelter yourself and your fire. You try with clothes and insulation to confine and hold the heat but everything—your house, your body—continually seeks the level of the external soup. You resist as well as you can, as long as you can; that's life.

The first thing to understand as you resist is that heat flows. It always flows toward something cooler. It seeks the uniform soup as follows:

- By conduction. The silver spoon conducts heat from the tea quickly, the wooden spoon slowly.

- By convection. Here a fluid picks up warmth from one surface (a stove, a radiator) and carries it elsewhere. The usual fluids are water and air (fluid in the sense of flowing), which carry warmth in our hot-air or hot-water heating systems.

- By radiation, which transfers heat from one object to another without contact. The sun warms by radiation. A stove warms by radiation. (But also by convection, and by conduction if you touch it.) Radiant energy travels at the speed of light in the form of infrared electromagnetic waves. Dark objects absorb this energy readily, light objects reflect much of it, which is why summer clothes come in light colors, and why aluminum foil protects the turkey from overexposure in the oven.

Stand in front of a fire. Heat radiates toward you and the front of your body grows warm. But your back, with the darkened window behind it and winter outside, grows cold; you are radiating your own warmth to the outdoors.

In warming a room the tendency is to think of warming air. The air is what you are *in*. So if you are cold the air must be cold. Not so—air has little mass. It holds little heat. Your surroundings—walls, floor, ceiling, furniture—do have mass and do hold heat. If warm enough they will radiate that heat at you; if cold you will feel cold.

The temperature must be higher for you to feel comfortable in a room warmed by hot air, compared with one warmed by radiant methods. Blown hot air creates indoor weather; it stratifies in a room. There may be a 10°F or greater temperature difference between floor and ceiling. Hot head, cold feet. This differential causes constant air movement, indoor weather. Hot air gusts up out of the register and moves to the ceiling. Then it moves to the walls, cools, falls to the floor. Cool drafts at ankle level flow to the cool air register and return to the furnace. Moving air, even moving warm air, cools you. That's the evaporation effect, the wind-chill effect; you feel cooler in moving air at 60° than in still air at 60°. A blown hot-air heating system is in this sense self-defeating, because it requires more energy than a radiant (still-air) system to make you comfortable. Blown hot air heat sells on the basis of its lower cost. Radiant systems may cost more to install. They pay off in warming you with less energy.

In a radiant system, there is an absolute minimum of indoor weather. Liverpool Cathedral installed a system that warmed its stone floor from below. The floor itself became one vast low-temperature radiator. Between two points, one four feet above the floor and the other ninety-seven feet above it, there is a temperature difference of only 1½°F. Without a sharp temperature differential, interior weather all but ceases. No drafts. The effect is an improvement in comfort, and very likely in health as well. It is a truth some ancient builders may have understood better than we. Big masonry stoves are primarily low-level radiant

Figure 165 Indian women carry bark fuel gathered in the forests of Ecuador. Indians of the Andean highlands have no wood at all, and use manure or grass ropes for fuel. FAO photo by M. Gonzales de Moya.

heaters. So are the ancient subfloor systems. They create warmth with a minimum of indoor weather.

HOUSES AND HEAT

Three basic questions arise in the realm of housewarming: How to generate the heat, how to distribute it, how to keep it from escaping the building.

Today the answer to the escape problem is urged upon one and all: Tighten up, chink the cracks, and insulate. But too often little attention gets paid to how the insulating is done. Typical North American construction places the insulation in the wall cavity just beyond the inner skin of the room. Most commonly this inner skin is sheetrock or plaster. When you heat such a house, you heat the air inside it, the furniture, the sheetrock, dogs, cats, resident citizens—whatever lies inside the insulation barrier. But in terms of mass that may not amount to much. The better part of the building's mass does not get warm because you have placed the insulation *between* the heat and that mass. As a result the house tends to act like a tin oven: It heats and cools quickly.

Now suppose you put the insulation on the *outside* of the house wall. Then the whole wall and not just the sheetrock can store heat. You've improved thermal stability: The greater the mass, the longer it takes to heat or cool off. Make the wall of masonry and you improve stability a lot more. By warming enough brickwork you can store heat to keep the house from freezing for days, even with the furnace shut down. Recall the Roman hypocaust, which took days to warm and a correspondingly long time to cool. Pueblo Indians use the same principle in their adobe buildings. So do people living in the many mud-brick houses of the Mideast and Asia.

House location also has a major effect on heating. Suppose a given building has a third of its heat loss through the windows, a third through walls and roof, and another third through infiltration, or air leaks. It has been shown that wind all by itself can double heat loss through single-pane glass, and raise to 75 percent the amount of heat lost by infiltration. All of which suggests how important it is to locate in a sheltered as well as sunny spot. If you can't find a sheltered spot, then cut the wind's effect by digging in, planting windbreaks, or any other way you can think of.

Earth-Sheltered Housing, Circa 1850

A man emerged from a hole in the ground and asked for our passports.

I was astonished.

Looking around, I observed two or three small conical elevations resembling magnified ant-hills with a large hole by the side of each.

"What are these little mounds?" I inquired of Aristas.

"They are Wallach houses," he replied. "The peasants call them *kolibes*. You will see them everywhere in the Danubian principalities."

"Eh bien! I understand: fuel is scarce on the Wallachian prairies and the Daco-Romans burrow into the bosom of Mother Earth in order to enjoy her warmth!"

"Oui, Monsieur!"

James O. Noyes, M.D., *Roumania*, New York, 1857.

Now if this makes you think the valley is a suitably sheltered spot, wait a moment. During the night dense, cold air, because of its greater weight, sinks to the valley floor, displacing warmer air, which rises. Temperatures on a valley floor will be well below those on surrounding hillsides. My own house is about halfway down a south-facing hill perhaps two hundred fifty vertical feet above the valley floor. On cold winter nights my thermometers will read ten to fifteen degrees above those in the valley below. Some so-called primitive peoples plant sensitive crops like squash on mounds, so that colder air will slip by below the plants and leave them unharmed. The same principle can be applied to housing. Off the hilltop and sheltered, but above the valley floor, is a worthwhile place to be.

DISTRIBUTION

Central heating systems distribute heat mechanically. Blowers move hot air, pumps drive hot water through pipes; heat reaches distant rooms from a central source. This system can be expensive, however, especially when remote rooms are little used.

Stoves are zone or area heaters. Most lack any mechanical means of distributing heat. They supply warmth at a specific location, where and when it is needed. The nineteenth-century household often had a large stove to warm a central living area and smaller stoves for occasional use in outlying rooms. It is more trouble to operate several stoves than one furnace, but it costs less to supply warmth only where and when needed.

If you are going to have central heat, building layout is not so important. The furnace system will pump heat almost anywhere. But if you design for stoves, building layout becomes very important. The A-frame, for example, was a silly idea to begin with; it becomes even sillier as the heat from your stove collects high overhead and you have to install a duct and blower to get it back down where you live. Cathedral ceilings offer the same difficulties, unless you install a warm-floor system, as at Liverpool Cathedral. The ultralong ranch house provides another sort of problem; heat rises without mechanical aid, but it does not travel well horizontally. So the long ranch house requires blowers to move air, or stoves at opposite ends of the house.

Houses divided into many small rooms present still another distribution difficulty. Think of a series of ponds linked by shallow channels. The shallowness of the channels limits the water flow from one pond to the next. Turn the situation upside down and you will understand about air movement between rooms. Warm air collects in a kind of pond in the upper part of the room. It can move into the next room only through the doorway. But the portion of wall above the doorway blocks the way; it acts like a dam holding back the warmest air.

The designer of a house to be heated by stoves, then, must take air circulation into account. Open construction will allow better air flow. Placing sections of a long house at successively higher levels may allow warm air to move horizontally.

Locating the stove is obviously crucial to heat distribution, in any house. Of course, you want the warmth of the main stove in the central living area, where you spend your time. So that is the best place to put it.

Unhappily, many people feel the stove belongs in the cellar with the furnace. There you lose the value of the stove's radiant warmth; you cannot get up next to it. Efficiency suffers; you lose heat via uninsulated cellar walls and floor. Finally, it is a nuisance to keep going downstairs to check the stove and feed it. Basements are a poor place for stoves, unless you happen to live there. Ancient tradition made hearth and stove central to family life, and that is where a source of heat should be, not in the cellar.

Another factor in stove location is the chimney effect. Any vertical shaft—a stairwell, spaces between studs in uninsulated walls—will act like a chimney. Warm air rises up the shaft. If you locate a stove next to the stairwell, much of the heat will go straight upstairs. Unless you like a hot bedroom and a cool parlor, that is probably not desirable.

COMPONENTS THAT MATCH

In the early upsurge of wood burning after 1974, many people closed up their fireplace openings. They put a piece of sheet metal across the opening, cut a hole in it and attached a stove. Often the old fireplaces so treated were rather large, and together with the chimney comprised tons of masonry. The chimney flue was correspondingly big, to accommodate the large volume of hot air that rose to warm turkeys in the sky whenever a cheery blaze burned on the hearth.

While looking for a stove to place on the open hearth, most people came to the same perfectly reasonable conclusion: The top of the fireplace opening was too low; only a small stove would fit on the hearth. So there arose a brisk trade in small stoves with flue outlets low enough to extend into the fireplace opening. Shortly thereafter, there arose as well a brisk trade in chimney-sweeping, as the flues plugged up with soot and caught fire.

During the fireplace era, with a big blaze on the hearth and 90 percent of the heat going up the chimney, there was little trouble with soot and creosote. All that heat warmed the flue so little soot formed and nobody needed a chimney sweep. Hook a small stove to the chimney and the situation changes dramatically. Now perhaps 45 percent of the heat goes up the chimney, the rest into the room. The stove is small so less heat is produced; the chimney is massive and there just is not enough heat coming through to keep it warm. The chimney remains cool and gases from an air-starved fire condense on the chimney walls, building up soot and creosote. In an old unlined chimney the creosote may penetrate weakened brickwork and create a truly unlovely and evil-smelling mess. Of course, it is also a dangerous mess, as many woodburners have learned, sometimes through the loss of their homes and even lives.

A large part of the problem here is that two components in the system, stove and chimney, are poorly matched. The chimney is too massive to be warmed by the small stove; the flue is too large for the volume of gases produced in the stove. Nothing works as it should in this situation, whether your stove is made of iron or masonry. The stove's smoke outlet and the chimney flue should be matched. I use a six-inch round flue, the smallest I can get, for a stove with a five-inch smoke outlet. Ideally, the chimney's flue lining should be insulated, so that it warms quickly and stays warm.

Pipe connectors between stove and chimney should:

- Be as short as possible and slope upward at least 15°.

- Be the same diameter as the stove's flue collar or a bit larger, never smaller. Pipe should be no larger in diameter than the chimney flue.

- Be of sturdy welded steel or tile. Avoid flimsy light-gauge metal; much of this falls below the standard of the National Fire Protection Association for thickness, and that standard is nothing to brag about. I have seen new pipe that meets the standard simply collapse and fall to the floor during use. My own standard for sturdiness is: Can you stand on the pipe without squashing it? The NFPA standard (24 gauge) is not up to this. I think the standard should be upgraded; I've seen a lot of creosote fires, and what they can do to pipe, and to a house. Twenty-four gauge pipe simply does not make it for safety.

THE "RIGHT" HEATING SYSTEM

Houses differ in design and construction. Heating needs differ from region to region. Anyone who attempts to generalize about the heating needs of others risks appearing half a fool, if not a whole one. But it is a risk worth taking, just to suggest some of the questions you should be asking about heating. For the answers you may want to find a competent heating contractor or consultant in your own area. If so, try to find someone who gains nothing from selling you a particular product. Be careful of the advice of neighbors unless they have broad and varied experience in wood burning. Virtually all wood burners will assure you their stove (or furnace) is a good one—simply great—right up to the day they sell the thing. It is not a question of deceit, just lack of experience and a wish to believe they have made a good choice.

Now as to the sort of questions you should be asking yourself, consider this: Suppose you have a large building to heat, say a New England colonial house. The building is big, the rooms smallish. The building thus calls for major heat, each room for minor heat. Air circulation is poor, insulation so-so. What do you do?

If you put a big stove in a small room, the room gets too hot. The tendency will

Figure 166   Women making dung cakes for fuel in an Indian village in Uttar Pradesh. Note cakes stacked to dry in background. FAO photo by P. Pittet.

be to reduce air supply to the fire to slow it down and cool the stove; this cuts efficiency, creates pollution, plugs the chimney.

If you put in a small stove the tendency may be to run it too hard, trying to force heat around to other rooms, which are cold. Overfiring may damage the small stove. It will lower efficiency, send-

ing too much heat up the chimney; you are running the air-movement engine too fast.

The solution for the big building with small rooms and poor air circulation may be central heat. That is why our ancestors thought it was such a great idea; it got the heat around better than stoves did. Another solution might be remodeling both to insulate and to produce better air circulation, so that a stove can readily warm the main living area. Whatever the solution, it should provide a balance between structure, heating apparatus, and the needs of the occupants.

Make certain the chimney flue is big enough, but not too big, for the stove or furnace attached. A neighbor of mine installed a $6,000 wood furnace system and hooked it to an existing chimney, only to find the flue too small to handle the smoke adequately. Necessity (lack of cash) may dictate that you use an existing massive chimney for a small stove. If so, remember that you are going to have to send quite a bit of heat up the chimney to warm the flue if the system is to work well, and if you are to avoid major creosote problems. This may affect the type of stove you buy and the way you use it. An old-fashioned antique iron stove that is not airtight may be your best bet; it will send plenty of heat up the flue and keep it warm. You are "wasting" some heat, but also getting the whole system to work better and reducing the risk of fire. Spending a little heat to buy safety is worth it.

Keep yourself in mind as a component, and not only your skills as a stove operator. My local paper contains frequent ads that read "Cast-iron stove for sale; excellent stove in good condition; switching to wood-burning furnace." The ads were placed by people who found they lacked time or desire to tend an iron

stove as often as necessary (which can be six or seven or more times a day in cold weather). There is a trend toward central heat today among those who bought iron stoves a few years back. These people have learned something about themselves after the early romance of wood heat wore off. What they want now is something they can tend once or twice a day, perhaps even less—like a furnace, or a masonry stove.

FIRING AND FUEL

Firing technique may vary according to the design of the masonry stove. Here I'll take up only the wood-burning models designed for intermittent firing, once or twice a day. The continuous combustion models that burn coal or coke or briquettes follow standard firing techniques for these fuels, and information on these is readily available.

Though there are minor differences in firing from one type of masonry stove to the next, the principle is always the same: Fire quickly at high temperature with sufficient air so that all gases burn; *never* use the slow-burn, air-starvation technique employed to get long burns out of iron stoves.

Take the firing instructions for a typical Swedish stove as an example: Starting with a cold stove, build a fire of paper and softwood kindling only. The stove's doors and damper are fully open. The hot kindling fire warms the body of

the stove and drives the cold air plug out of the chimney. You know when the plug is gone because the color of the fire changes from smoky orange to vivid and smokeless yellow-white. Then it is time to add hardwood. Fill the firebox, close the stove doors (air now enters through a regulator in the door), and close the damper about halfway. Adjust the air supply to produce a fire hot enough to consume the gases and give good combustion, but not so hot as to draw heat unnecessarily into the chimney. *The wood should burn as long as possible while still burning completely.*

It is easy to see that in this type of firing, the role of the stove operator is important. Too much air wastes heat; too little air will lower combustion efficiency and produce soot. Many vertical east European and Finnish stoves are fired in the same way as the Swedish models, and similar care in operation is required during the firing period. Kari Mäkelä, a Finnish expert on heating, estimated that the efficiency of these vertical stoves will be 70 to 90 percent, the difference depending entirely on the skill of the operator.

In a Swedish stove the kindling fire may take anywhere from a few minutes to half an hour, depending on stove and chimney. Hardwood firing thereafter may take an hour or two. As the fire burns down to coals, the scrupulous operator gradually shuts down the chimney damper, applying the sniff test described in chapter 9 to determine how far to shut it at any given moment. Close attention to this detail produces peak efficiency.

It is clear that the Swedish, Finnish, and east European stoves operated in this way require attention and skill to perform at their best. But this attention need be applied only during the one or two rather brief firing periods each day. And if you wish to pay less attention and thus sacrifice a few points in efficiency, the results will still be good.

Austrian stoves (and central European stoves generally) follow a somewhat

Figure 167 Afghan boy gathering weed stalks and brush for fuel, a necessity for many people in treeless regions. FAO photo.

simpler procedure, with less dependence on human skills. The traditional wood-burning tile stove is fired with the door open until the wood has burned down to coals. No minor adjustments of door or damper, the fire goes full bore until the yellow flames are gone and nothing remains but glowing coals. Then the door is shut tight and the stove left until the next firing twelve or twenty-four hours later.

How long you fire depends on the size of the stove, whether it was cold to begin with, and how much heat you need. A big stove starting cold may require a second fuel loading to get up to the necessary temperature. But if it takes two hours to get a cold stove up to the proper heat level, it will take less time and fuel to get it back up there on a second firing twelve hours later. That's because it hasn't cooled down completely, nor has the chimney.

FUELS

Wood for the masonry stove should be of uniform size, so that all pieces burn down to coals at the same time. The stove can then be shut down to hold in heat, without waiting for the one or two fat chunks left to be reduced to coals. A common rule of thumb is that wood for the masonry stove be no larger than three inches in diameter. In many parts of Europe fuel consists of small sticks or even twigs tied together in a bundle.

These are used both in masonry stoves and baking ovens. This is an age-old practice that conserves bigger wood for other uses.

Small pieces of wood create good combustion conditions. There is good mixing of fuel and air; high temperatures build quickly to burn the gases. In contrast the big chunks often used in iron stoves create rather poor combustion conditions. The fire of small pieces of wood tends to be quick and hot; that fueled with a few big chunks is slower and cooler, just what you don't want for efficient combustion.

Wood for the masonry stove requires more preparation, to reduce it to smaller pieces, but high efficiency reduces the total amount of wood needed. Wood that many would consider waste—limbs, branches, even twigs—can be burned. A dealer near me sells hardwood cut and split for $80 a cord. His "limb wood" goes for less than half that and it is ideal for the masonry stove. So was the small-ish wood cut under coppice rotation in Europe in the past.

In parts of Europe, on the Hungarian or Russian plains, for example, little wood is available. Masonry stoves there have long been fired with straw, reeds, or weed stalks, as were some Roman hypocausts in the more distant past. Moravian settlers in Nebraska in the nineteenth century built Russian-style brick stoves and burned hay in them. Other Midwesterners, short of wood or buffalo chips for fuel, used specially built iron

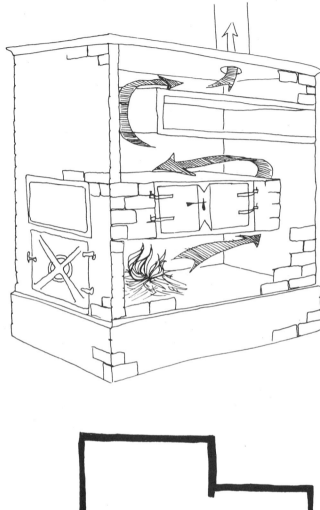

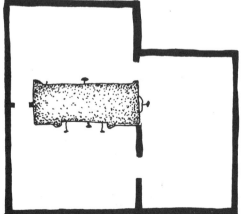

Figures 168 and 169   In the 1870s Mennonite farmers from the Black Sea region of Russia settled in Nebraska, where they built their traditional grass-burning stoves of brick. The size varied, but a typical model was six feet high, five feet long, and two and a half feet wide. Firebox dimensions were about 18 inches by 18 inches by 48 inches. Fuel was thrust in the door with a hay fork. J. D. Butler, who in 1878 described these stoves in *The Nebraska Farmer*, said that two or three firings per day, each lasting about twenty minutes, provided heat for cooking and comfort in a house measuring 27 feet by 48 feet. Construction materials were common brick, stone, and clay mixed with sand. Some families maintained one grass-burner indoors for winter warmth, and a second outdoors for summer baking. Figure 169 shows how the grass-burner could be located centrally to warm three rooms.

stoves that fed "twists" of hay from a magazine into the firebox. Even corn became fuel in some areas of the Midwest.

Although it can provide plenty of heat, hay has serious drawbacks. It is messy. Volumes of it stashed near the stove for convenience represent a huge fire risk. Hay-burning Nebraska pioneers sometimes lost their homes that way. Hay is not a fuel I recommend, except when burned with great care as an emergency fuel where there is no alternative. If one were going to consider hay as a basic fuel, then I think the way to do it would be to set up a hay-fired boiler in a building separate from the house; hot water could then be piped in for heating. Building and fuel storage in such a hay system ought to be carefully designed to minimize fire risks and to segregate such risks from the dwelling.

Trash is sometimes used as fuel. Some stove advertisers advise against burning trash in the stove. Others trumpet: "You can burn trash in our stove! Won't hurt it a bit!" They are anxious to make a sales point, to set their stove apart from those vaguely suspect—possibly effete?—models unsuited to trash burning.

Trash today often contains plastics. When burned these can develop gases corrosive to flues and stoves, not to mention lungs. One of the bright new "energy from trash" projects touted in the press had to shut down a while back in New York State. Nasty gases from burned plastic were being loosed on the community from its stacks. On a smaller scale, the trash-burning stove can create the same kind of trouble. So I would avoid trash as fuel. I like to put wood ashes on the garden, but would rather avoid residues from all those mysterious new inks and plastics.

CHIMNEY

Chimney fires have increased sharply with the revival of wood burning. Such fires are an unnecessary evil even with the use of airtight iron stoves; and they ought never to occur with a masonry stove. Still the problem remains, and some discussion seems advisable. Lately the rash of fires has focused new attention on chimney design, with special attention to two questions:

1. Safety. Is the chimney adequate to contain a 2,100°F creosote fire and keep it from spreading to the structure?

2. If the chimney is adequate, does the chimney in fact survive the fire in the sense of remaining sound for further use?

It is clear that many existing chimneys are not adequate for wood burning. They fail on both counts above. Underwriters' Laboratories of Canada has recently adopted more stringent standards for chimney design. In the U.S., Underwriters' Laboratories is considering similarly strict standards. With all this in mind, a few suggestions.

- If you intend to use an existing masonry chimney, look it over with care or have an expert do so. The chimney should have a tile liner or its equivalent. It should meet code requirements. The mortar joints should be sound. Have the chimney repaired or replaced if it fails on any count.

- If you intend to install a prefabricated chimney (any of the several metal models available), use one that meets the new Canadian standards or the new U.S. standards when adopted. Several types now available in the U.S. meet Canadian standards. Use only the insulated prefab metal models, not the air-cooled variety.

- If you are building a new masonry chimney, make certain you have a mason who understands what is required. Many do not. A tile liner requires space to expand, especially when subjected to a chimney fire. Many masons overlook or ignore this. The liner then cracks during a flue fire, making the chimney unsound.

- If you are building a masonry chimney, consider a way often used in Europe: Insulate the space between the flue liner and the chimney's outer wall. This has the effect of keeping the flue warm and of improving draft. It also permits the liner room to expand against the insulation, even during a chimney fire. A common insulation used in Scandinavia consists of six parts expanded clay to one of Portland cement. The mix is poured into the space between liner and the chimney's outer (brick or block) casing. Expanded clay may not be readily available, but some other mineral-based insulation surely will be: vermiculite, perlite, expanded shale, or expanded slate.

- Use one flue per stove. Use a flue as large as you need but no larger. The following table prepared by Underwriters' Laboratories of the U.S. may be useful in matching heat output to flue size.

Chimney Flue Size	Btu/hr	Wood lb/hr	Coal lb/hr
6"	97,000	12.1	6
7"	131,000	16.5	8.25
8"	172,400	21.6	10.8
9"	218,000	27.3	13.6
10"	270,000	33.8	16.9

Two final chimney suggestions:

- Locate the chimney entirely within the house. Then you will benefit from whatever heat it may radiate. Also this will reduce draft or condensation problems that often develop when chimneys are built outside.

- To the extent that a masonry chimney stores and radiates heat, it can also transfer that heat outdoors at the point where the chimney passes through the roof. Some form of insulating masonry built into the chimney just below the roof can greatly limit this loss. Refractory companies can provide insulating brick. Many block companies produce concrete block made with light aggregate which has an insulating effect.

The wood consumption figures in the following table are of necessity highly generalized. But for the uninitiated, they will give a rough guide to wood fuel use in different regions of the U.S.

The following table gives for ten U.S. regions the approximate yearly heating requirement in millions of BTUs (MBTU) for a typical household. Again the figures are generalized, and assume the "standard house" described for the table at left.

Annual Estimated Wood Fuel Requirements for Ten Regions*

Region 1	Maine, New Hampshire, Vermont, Massachusetts, Connecticut, Rhode Island	6.87 cords
Region 2	New York, New Jersey	5.46 cords
Region 3	Pennsylvania, Maryland, West Virginia, Virginia, Delaware	4.86 cords
Region 4	Alabama, Florida, Georgia, Kentucky, Mississippi, North Carolina, South Carolina, Tennessee	2.77 cords
Region 5	Minnesota, Wisconsin, Michigan, Illinois, Indiana, Ohio	6.66 cords
Region 6	Texas, New Mexico, Oklahoma, Arkansas, Louisiana	2.92 cords
Region 7	Kansas, Missouri, Iowa, Nebraska	5.84 cords
Region 8	Montana, North Dakota, South Dakota, Wyoming, Utah, Colorado	6.98 cords
Region 9	California, Nevada, Arizona, Hawaii	3.36 cords
Region 10	Idaho, Washington, Oregon, Alaska	6.41 cords

* The figures above are based on the assumption that 20,000 Btu were required to heat each household per degree day, in a stove of 75 percent efficiency—a level rarely reached in iron stoves today but quite possible in masonry stoves. The figures assume a "standard 20 × 40 house with normal insulation, in which an ambient temperature of 65° is maintained." The table is based on material in a report, *The Use of Wood for Fuel*, prepared for the Department of Energy under the direction of Dr. Ralph M. Bradburd of Williams College.

Required MBTU per Household*

D.O.E. Region	October–December	January	February–May	Annual Total
Region 1 (Me., N.H., Vt., Mass., Conn., R.I.)	51.52	25.84	61.76	139.12
Region 2 (N.Y., N.J.)	39.86	21.73	49.08	110.67
Region 3 (Pa., Md., W.Va., Va., Del.)	36.56	19.46	42.42	98.44
Region 4 (Ala., Fla., Ga., Ky., Miss., N.C., S.C., Tenn.)	22.02	12.52	21.46	56.00
Region 5 (Minn., Wis., Mich., Ill., Ind., Ohio)	49.64	26.56	58.76	134.96
Region 6 (Tex., N.Mex., Okla., Ark., La.)	23.14	13.98	22.10	59.22
Region 7 (Kans., Mo., Iowa, Nebr.)	43.96	24.86	49.36	118.18
Region 8 (Mont., N.Dak., S.Dak., Wyo., Utah, Colo.)	53.80	28.25	59.38	141.43
Region 9 (Calif., Nev., Ariz., Hawaii)	26.04	13.82	28.18	68.04
Region 10 (Idaho, Wash., Oreg., Ala.)	50.62	24.78	53.80	129.92

* Based on 20,000 Btu per degree day. Monthly degree day figures from U.S. Department of Commerce, *Climatic Atlas of the United States*. Table from D.O.E. report prepared under direction of Dr. Ralph M. Bradburd.

Effective Btu per Unit of Fuel*			
	Btu per unit	Assumed Heating Efficiency of System	Units required per one million effective Btu's
Electricity	3,412 Btu/kw	100%	293 kw/MBTU
Oil	140,000 Btu/gal	75%	9.5 gal/MBTU
Gas	1 MBTU/1000 ft^3	75%	1,333 ft^3/MBTU
Coal	28 MBTU/ton	75%	.05 ton/MBTU
Wood	27 MBTU/cord	75%	.05 cord/MBTU

* Table from D.O.E. report prepared under direction of Dr. Ralph M. Bradburd.

PART 3

TECHNICAL DETAILS

Oils are powerful fuels, but the high price of refined petroleum, the oil generally preferred, precludes its widespread use for many purposes for which it is suitable.

Encyclopaedia Britannica Eleventh edition, New York, 1910.

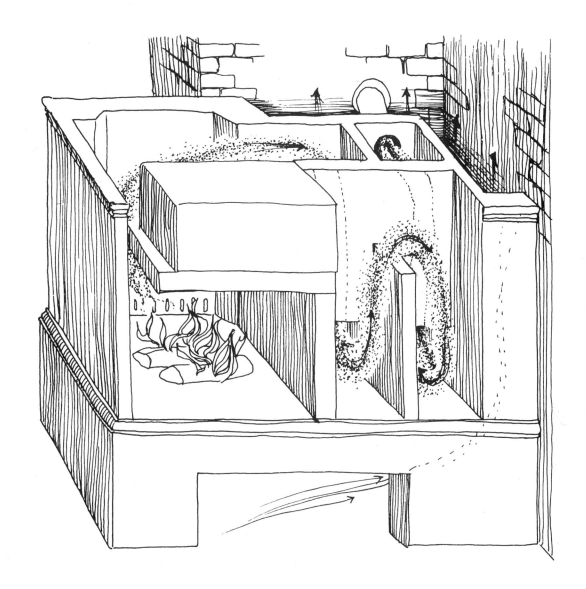

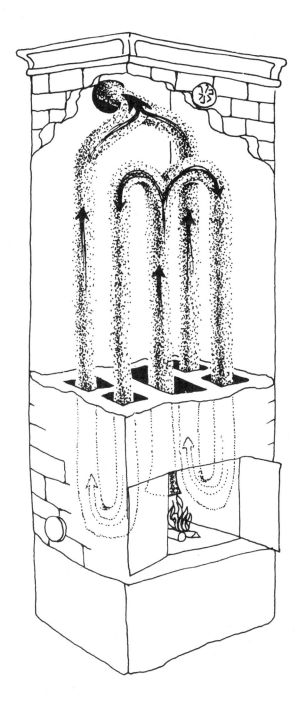

Chapter 13

Masonry Stove Design and Construction

Beware of the notion that there is some finally "correct" way to build a masonry stove. There is none. Techniques vary from one country to the next. Climate, housing, and culture affect the outcome. As with automobiles and beds, different models fill different needs. Certain principles behind masonry stove design remain similar from one region to the next, and it is these I have tried to explore.

Take what follows as a guide, then, and not some final pronouncement, frozen for all time, as to what the masonry stove must be; flexibility is one of the most appealing aspects of masonry stove design.

In this chapter I have tried to outline certain rules of thumb for masonry stove construction, the fundamentals. I have concentrated on Austrian designs because I have more detail available on these. Also, much work has been done in Austria in the twentieth century to bring tile-stove design to new levels of effectiveness. This does not mean designs from other countries are less worthy. Some are superb and no doubt equal to the best in Austria. But in general, Austrian design rules will apply to them as well.

I have not tried to cover every construction question that may arise, nor

Figure 170   On Palm Sunday in 1939. Erika Groth-Schmachtenberger was taking photographs in the small village of Thaur in the Austrian Tyrol. Looking for old tile stoves, she asked about in a tavern and, "A peasant drinking there his pot of beer said I should come along with him to his house, where he would have such a kachelofen. We went there together and he—in his Sunday dress—laid himself down on the oven bench, putting his hat aside." Thus this photo of a world that was even then slowly being lost. "I may also mention, " the photographer said, "that one can mount to the top of the oven and lie down on the wooden platform, to get warmed up." Photo by Erika Groth-Schmachtenberger.

offered a primer in the mason's arts. The information is readily available elsewhere, and space is lacking here. Furthermore, I have assumed most readers will and should seek expert help in stove design and construction. Josef Thurner, when he was head of Austria's tile-stove builders' guild, told me repeatedly, "You can't build a stove from a book." I have to agree. Certain masonry techniques are best learned from practice and an experienced teacher. Mr. Thurner's concern was that poor design, poorly built and amateurish stoves might give the masonry stove a bad name in the U.S. before its many virtues could be recognized. It is a legitimate concern. The fact is that some stoves are being built today in North America by people who possess much enthusiasm but little knowledge or experience. More will be built under the same sponsorship; it is the way of the world, and humility does not permit the notion one can change it. Such are the virtues of masonry stoves, fortunately, that their owners tend to rave about even comparatively poor specimens. Handled with knowledge and care, even these may perform very well.

Take the following for what it is, then: a survey of rules and methods that have been found useful in Europe. These should be applied with the normal attention to basic construction and masonry techniques, and to local codes. In developing a design for your own dwelling, seek the aid of the knowledgeable in all of these spheres.

TRADITIONAL STOVE MATERIALS

Traditional stove materials are brick, clay, tile, and sand. Stone should be included, with the note that it is seldom used today, and that special care must be taken in its use.

If you look a bit more closely, you notice that the materials boil down to clay: clay mortar, clay tile, clay brick. (The sand is used only in small quantities as a component in mortar.) There is a reason. Where all parts are made of clay, all parts will expand and contract in harmony. *In building any masonry stove, the materials must expand or contract at the same rate. Otherwise heat will tear the structure apart, just like ice cracking an engine block.* This is a fundamental rule in masonry stove design. It is one reason European builders never use ordinary Portland cement in stoves; it will crack.

Any metal (i.e. doors) must be used with care; its greater rate of expansion and contraction can damage the stove. The same applies to stone. Stone has been used in stoves because of low cost, availability, and good heat-storage capacity. But rock of the wrong type can crack or disintegrate under heat, even explode if it holds trapped water. Also, the expansion rate will differ from the stove's clay parts. It is best to use any stone loosely stacked in the stove, as people of the Baltic area did in their kilns and sauna heaters. Then there is room for expansion and contraction. Test any stone in fire before you use it. Dry it thoroughly; make certain it won't explode or disintegrate because of the sudden expansion of trapped water.

Brick comes in many forms, with different responses to heat. Common red building brick, for example, will melt, crack, or spall somewhere around 1,100°C (2,012°F). Perhaps you have noticed the deterioration of common brick in a fireplace. Chips flake off; the bricks begin to look eaten away. That's spalling. So where high temperature develops, use firebrick. Tile-stove fireboxes are completely lined with it. Often much of the smoke channel system will be lined with firebrick as well, though firebrick thickness might well be reduced beyond the firebox. Firebrick is made of clay, like common brick, but it is a grade known as fireclay that melts at a higher temperature and forms a dense, hard brick. For example, kaolin, one form of fireclay, melts in its pure form at 1,785°C (3,245°F).

The tile used in stoves is terra cotta. Because it covers only the stove's outer surface, it does not have to withstand very high temperatures. Firebrick protects it on the inside. The use of firebrick is essential because terra cotta does not withstand high temperatures.

MORTAR

All over Europe, ancient and modern stove builders have used the same kind of mortar, though the formulas for mixing it vary. The mix is always part sand and part clay, with the amount of sand varying according to the quality of the clay. One Russian formula calls for half sand and half clay if the clay is "greasy," or for less sand if the clay is "thin," meaning that it already has some sand in it. Water is mixed in until the mixture turns to a smooth mud just short of pouring consistency. The mix should

Figure 171 Early masonry stoves were often all-clay. This one, now in the folk arts museum in Innsbruck, Austria, came originally from a Tyrolean farmhouse.

stand for twenty-four hours before use. Between bricks the Russian mason calls for one-half centimeter of mortar. That's a good deal less mortar than used in laying ordinary building brick; masons in the U.S. typically lay a mortar bed twice as deep.

Swedish and Finnish formulas call for one part clay and three to five parts sand. Again, the sand volume varies according to the quality of the clay. Sand grains should be no more than three millimeters in diameter.

European stove mortar is made from *unfired* clay. Many stove builders get mortar clay from a brickyard. They use broken or defective brick cast aside before firing in the kiln, then dissolve the clay or grind it into powder. In America potters building kilns sometimes make a clay mortar based on two parts fireclay to one of grog or sand, with grog preferred. Grog is clay that has been fired and then ground up. Clay shrinks at least 5 percent when fired, and mixing grog with unfired clay reduces shrinkage.

Aside from the expansion/contraction factor, there is another reason to use clay mortar. A stove built with it can be readily dismantled and rebuilt without damage to components. Tile stoves can thus be rebuilt and kept in use for generations. Cleanout bricks or tiles can be removed easily and replaced as needed. Ordinary Portland cement would be less forgiving; heat would break it down. Tiles would tend to break as the stove was dismantled.

PLASTER SURFACES

In Sweden and Finland, the surface of brick stoves is often coated with a plaster. G. E. Asp in his book on masonry stove construction in Finland has outlined two approaches.

In one method, Asp suggests leaving each brick joint on the surface of the stove unmortared to a depth of two centimeters. This provides a gap for the plaster to key into, as it does with lath. The result is a better bond with the brick. Asp suggests using an ordinary lime plaster applied about one centimeter thick; a small amount of water glass may be mixed with the plaster. An alternative mix is one part cement, three to four parts lime, and eight to ten parts fine sand.

The second method is to cover the stove surface with wire lath or equivalent, standing three to five millimeters away from the brick surface. Coat this with lime cement mortar and when it has dried brush it with water glass. Make a final coat of ordinary lime plaster, which you can turn snow white by mixing in white marble sand.

MODERN MATERIALS

The most elaborate modern tile stove is really just a clay oven, differing greatly in detail but not in kind from clay ovens thousands of years old. Brick, clay mortar, and tile are likely to continue as basic masonry stove building materials. But there are now exciting possibilities in other materials, especially those known to kiln and furnace builders as castable refractories. A refractory material like fireclay withstands heat well. A castable refractory is simply one that can be cast in a mold. Like cement, it is poured into a form to harden. Potters use castable refractories to make kiln parts and shapes too complex to produce easily with brick. Sometimes whole kilns are cast. The steel industry uses castables to line blast furnaces.

Kiln builders also have available an array of manufactured mortars that withstand high temperature. These are not necessarily superior to traditional stove mortars of Europe, but they may have special virtues for certain areas. For example, cements that remain flexible under heat may be used to fill expansion cracks where metal and masonry join. Refractory cements can also be handy if you are unable to make your own mortar out of clay.

The subject of castable refractories and high-heat mortars is too broad to cover here, but I can suggest three books:

Kilns by Daniel Rhodes, Chilton Book Co., Philadelphia, 1968.

The Kiln Book by Frederick L. Olsen, Keramos Books, Bassett, Calif., 1973.

Kiln Building with Space-Age Materials by Frank A. Colson, Van Nostrand Reinhold, New York, 1975.

STOVE SIZE AND MASS

A big iron stove will weigh three hundred to five hundred pounds. A small masonry stove may weigh fifteen hundred to three thousand pounds. (I'm speaking of built-in-place stoves here, not portable tile stoves.) A two-story masonry stove, built recently in New Hampshire by Gustav Jung of Vienna, weighed twelve thousand pounds. That's about as much as the weight of four moderate-size automobiles. A stove of that size ought ideally to be designed for and built with the structure. Substantial footings are essential to support the weight. Perhaps the stove should be built so that its radiating surfaces project into more than one room. On the other hand, a big masonry stove, one capable of very substantial heat output, *can* be built into an existing structure. It is a little more trouble, but by no means impossible. You'll need patience, some money, and a capable mason.

To repeat some general principles that affect size:

- Greater mass gives a stove more heat-storage capacity.

- Greater wall thickness slows the stove's response, the speed with which it delivers heat.

- The correct balance between heat-storage capacity and response speed depends on climate, house, and one's habits.

- Cold climates call for more massive stoves to store more heat and to reduce stress on the masonry.

- Moderate climates call for less massive stoves. Speed of response becomes more important where there are sudden changes in weather.

- All stoves are intended to be area heaters, not central heaters. To distribute heat widely from a stove, you'll require mechanical means (pumps, blowers) or good natural air circulation in the house.

Tile-stove walls in Europe vary in width from six to fifteen centimeters, or roughly two and three-eighths to six inches. Most tile-stove walls today are seven to ten centimeters thick, or three to four inches. Five centimeters of this represents the depth of tile; the rest is mortar and firebrick backing the tile.

The following material comes primarily from two Austrian stove designers of long experience, Gustav Jung and Josef Thurner. Additional material comes from the book *Wood Burning* by Hans Winkelmann, formerly director general of the Swiss Forestry Office; and from Kari Mäkelä, of the Finnish Building Institute.

The first step in figuring stove size is to calculate the heating requirement of the room. There are various methods of doing this and if you have one of your own that you like, by all means use it. One way used in Austria is to take a factor from the following table and multiply it by the air volume of the room in cubic meters.

Rooms	Heat Required	
	In Watts per Cubic Meters per Hour (W/m³/hr)	In Kcal per Cubic Meter per Hour (Kcal/m³/hr)
Room with one exterior wall	35–40	30–35
Room with one exterior wall plus unheated adjoining rooms	45–50	40–45
Room with two exterior walls, facing south or west	50–55	45–50
Room with two exterior walls, facing east or north	65–70	55–60
Bathroom with north or east exposure	80–90	70–80

Figure 172 The massive whitewashed clay stoves of east Europe stored vast amounts of heat. This Polish model served for heating, cooking and baking. (After K. Kwasniewski.)

In general, for bedrooms the next lower factor should be chosen; for bathrooms, the next higher.

The table on page 155 assumes certain conditions:

1. That the heat transfer quotient per square meter of surface of house wall, at a temperature differential of 1°C (1.8°F), lies on average between 0.9 and 1.40 watts, or between 0.8 and 1.20 Kcal.

2. That the portion of window area not be abnormal; at least 10 percent of the floor area is considered normal for window area.

3. That rooms are heated continuously, without long interruption; otherwise the next higher factor should be used.

4. The next higher factor should be chosen if the house site is: (a) shaded; (b) very windy; (c) more than 1,500 meters above sea level; (d) if indoor-outdoor temperature differences greater than 35°C can be expected.

As an example, assume that a room with one exterior wall plus adjoining unheated rooms (factor of 50 from the table) is to be heated by a tile stove. The air volume of the room is seventy-five cubic meters. The heating requirement of the room is $75m^3$ (room volume) × 50 (factor) = 3,750 watts.

The next step requires a figure for the heat output per hour per square meter of surface area for each type of stove that might be used to heat the room. This of course is an average figure, dependent on how the stove is run over a cycle of several hours; it serves only to give an approximate idea of the heating surface necessary in a given set of circumstances.

In the case of the tile stove above, the heat output per square meter assumes a surface temperature averaging 70°C (158°F). It also assumes a wall thickness of nine or ten centimeters, and a wall weight of 150 to 165 kilograms per square meter. Now suppose you add more wood to the fire and maintain an average surface temperature of 90° to 95°C (194° to 203°F). Then the heat output of the stove would increase to 1,000 kilocalories per hour per square meter ($Kcal/hr/m^2$) from the 800 kcal/hr/m² available at 70°C. Stress on the stove increases as well.

Stove Type	Heat Output per Square Meter in Watts	Heat Output per Square Meter in Kilocalories
Finnish brick stove with 12.3-cm thick wall	600/m²	500/m²
Brick or plastered brick stoves (central Europe)	700/m²	600/m²
Tile stoves	930/m²	800/m²
Iron firebox in tile stove, at maximum output	4,650/m²	4,000/m²

In very rough terms, a masonry stove must have four to eight times the surface area of an iron stove to provide equivalent heat output. The thicker the stove wall, the more suface area required.

Now back to the calculations. We had established a heating requirement for the $75m^3$ room of 3,750 watts. To figure the surface area of the stove required to heat the room, use the following formula:

$$\frac{R}{O} = S$$

R stands for the heating requirement of the room.

O stands for heat output of stove per square meter.

S stands for total heating surface of the stove.

In this case,

$$\frac{3,750 \text{ W}}{930 \text{ W/m}^2} = 4m^2 \text{ heating surface.}$$

To take another example:

$150m^3$ (room volume) × 50 (factor) = 7,500 watts required
7,500 W ÷ 930 W/m² (tile-stove heat output) = $8m^2$ surface

A third example shows how required heating surface falls with the use of the iron firebox to meet the same 7,500 watt requirement for the $150m^3$ room above:

7,500 W ÷ 4,650 W/m² = $1.6m^2$ firebox heating surface

This suggests why, where larger heat output is required, the iron firebox compromise comes into tile-stove construction in central Europe: It sharply reduces the size of the structure required. There is a corresponding decline in the quality of the heat, with more convection and less radiation with the firebox. Still the results are an improvement over ordinary iron-stove heat.

One more vital point on stove surface: You've noticed from the illustrations that tile stoves are generally raised above the floor on legs or arches. This is done primarily so that air can circulate beneath the stove; the bottom of the stove then becomes a heat-radiating surface. The idea is to expose all surfaces of the stove so that they can radiate. Where a stove sits flat on the floor, or is built against an outside wall, radiating surface is lost and heat output reduced. All of the masonry stoves I have seen built in the U.S. to date lose one radiating surface at least (the bottom) in this way.

FIREBOXES

The size of fireboxes, their configuration, and the airflow pattern within them, are crucial in stove design, especially perhaps in masonry stoves. Nevertheless it is a neglected subject. An early tendency in the U.S. was to make fireboxes so large that combustion efficiency suffered. Consider for a moment a hypothetical tile stove with five square meters of surface area. Gustav Jung's rule of thumb states that there should be four hundred square centimeters of firebox floor space for each square meter of stove surface. If a stove has five square meters of surface area, then the firebox floor should cover two thousand square centimeters. The height of the firebox in this instance, according to Mr. Jung, should be at least seventy centimeters. One rule I've heard states that no firebox for wood burning should be less than fifty centimeters high, or about twenty inches. But a height of seventy to eighty centimeters is considered desirable;

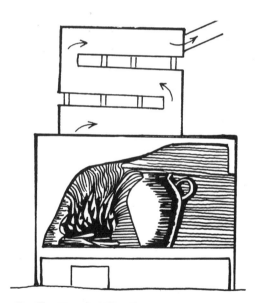

Figure 173 Smoke channels came into use for improving efficiency in European stoves during the Little Ice Age, as in this design by Franz Kessler. The firebox often served for cooking and baking as well as for the fire.

that's about 27½ to 31½ inches. I've heard of fireboxes as high as 153 centimeters, or about sixty inches.

In the modern central European stove, then, firebox height is virtually always greater than length or breadth. The theory is that low-ceilinged fireboxes, so common in iron stoves today, promote low efficiency, creosote, and high fuel consumption. The high firebox results in better mixing of fuel and air for effective combustion. If you think about it, this makes sense.

Below are some typical dimensions for Austrian tile-stove fireboxes:

Length (inches)	Width	Height
15½	13¾	21½
16	14	25½
18½	17½	25½
21	15½	24½
42½	17¼	53

The last measurements on the list belong to the firebox of the twelve-thousand-pound two-story model built in New Hampshire by Mr. Jung. Note that in all cases above, height is greater than breadth, yet in most iron stoves sold today it is the reverse: firebox length great-

ly exceeds height. A typical iron-stove firebox might measure twenty-six inches long by fifteen inches wide by fourteen inches high. The iron-stove firebox twenty inches high is rare indeed today.

Stove advertising today often pictures the large firebox as a good thing: bigger is better. In the eyes of most stove buyers the fuel door that takes great chunks of wood is also superior. A friend of mine, Walter Smith, suggested the ultimate in this direction: putting chimneys on old vans and advertising them as stoves that take ten-foot wood. Biggest and best of all! But size is decidedly a mixed blessing.

In a masonry stove, remember, the objective is a hot fire—rapid and intense combustion that burns all fuel. Vast fireboxes and great chunks of wood do not promote this objective. Big pieces of wood burn slowly; temperatures in the firebox then fall below levels necessary for good combustion. Where the firebox is a great cavern, there is simply more of it to heat, more of it to maintain at high temperature.

What is needed, again, is balance. The firebox must be large enough for the stove, yet not so large that the firebox itself is slow to warm. Avoid overkill. Remember, the goal is to warm a room or rooms, not to fire the boilers of the Titanic or practice suttee.

A particularly vital concept in masonry stove design is the "floating" firebox. (See figure 183 in the appendix.) By this I

Figure 174 Early metallurgists oriented their stoves to take advantage of the wind for improved combustion. Soon the bellows came into use for making the fire burn better, as in this drawing from medieval England. Today a power blower may fill the same role, providing more efficient combustion.

mean a firebox that is structurally separate from the outer walls of the stove. The firebox is subject to greater heat. Its components expand more. The structural separation accommodates this greater expansion so that the stove is not damaged by it. Some central European stove builders place corrugated cardboard (about one-quarter inch thick) between the outer wall of the firebox and any adjoining part of the stove structure. When the stove is fired, this cardboard turns to ash, leaving an air space around the firebox to allow for expansion.

One device used in central Europe that I have not heard of elsewhere is the gas slot. This is a small smoke passage that runs directly from the top of the firebox to the chimney flue, bypassing the longer smoke-channel system. This is a safety device. Its function is to carry off gases that might otherwise accumulate in the stove's firebox if the damper were closed prematurely. When gases accumulate, there is a risk of having them explode if air is let into the firebox suddenly. The phenomenon will be familiar to many wood and coal burners who use iron stoves. The gas slot eliminates the risk in masonry stoves. A rule of thumb calls for a gas slot of three square centimeters for each square meter of stove surface area. But in practice slots twice that size are often used.

GRATES

Traditional tile and masonry stoves were built without grates. Old-time builders will tell you they are unnecessary. But then uncertainty enters. The Swiss engineer W. Hausler, in his valuable book, *Technisches Handbuch des Hausbrandes,* states that grates unquestionably improve stove efficiency (better air/fuel mixing). On the other hand, says Mr. Hausler, tile stoves have proven very efficient without them. What it boils down to, then, is that until the question is further elucidated, you pay your money and take your choice. If you burn coal in a continuously fired masonry stove, you certainly need a grate. If you burn wood in the standard intermittently fired model, you can get along fine without a grate.

SMOKE CHANNELS

The common rule for determining smoke-channel length within the stove is to allow one meter of channel for each meter of stove surface area. Josef Thurner suggested that sections of channel where smoke travels downward be counted double; that is, one meter of downward channel should be counted as two meters. The greater the length of smoke channel, of course, the taller the chimney must be to produce adequate draft. Mr. Thurner offered the following table as a means of relating chimney height to channel length.

Chimney Height (meters)	Smoke-Channel Length (meters)
3	1.5
4	2.5
5	3.5
6	4.5
7	5.5
8	6.5

Typical cross-section area for a tile stove chimney in Austria would be three hundred fifty to four hundred square centimeters. The table above assumes a chimney flue twenty by twenty centi-

meters, which is the most common. Flues as large as twenty-five by twenty-five centimeters are in use. Mr. Thurner believes seventeen by seventeen centimeters should be the minimum, and I have heard of flues as small as fourteen by fourteen centimeters.

As gases emerge from the firebox, they are at their hottest, expanded and requiring more space. In fact these gases may have three times the volume of the air that entered the firebox. Moving on toward the chimney, the gases cool and contract; the smoke channels can thus taper and diminish in size as they progress. Mr. Jung uses a ratio of 1:2.5 to determine taper. That is, first determine the chimney flue size and then make the first smoke channel beyond the firebox 2.5 times larger. If the chimney flue were four hundred square centimeters, then the first smoke channel would be one thousand square centimeters. The channels would then taper to four hundred square centimeters at the chimney connection.

The opening from the firebox into the first channel is known in Austria as the *einbrand.* Typically Mr. Thurner would make this around six hundred square centimeters, never less than four hundred. I have heard another approach that calls for an einbrand 20 percent larger than the cross-section of the smoke channel immediately following it.

Hausler in Switzerland speaks of a typical reduction in channel size of 30 to

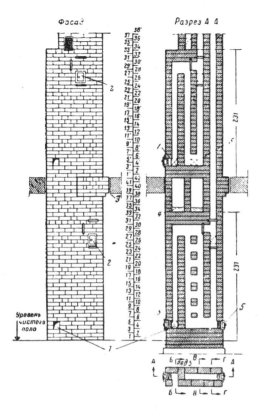

Figure 175 Smoke channels can be built into chimneys as well as stoves, as in this Russian heat storage chimney. The idea is to create an inferno in the stove and store the heat in the chimney. Dampers, closed after the fire dies, prevent the heat from escaping in this two-story model. From L.A. Semenov, courtesy of the Copyright Agency of the U.S.S.R.

40 percent between firebox and chimney. The smaller the channel cross-section, of course, the slower the progress of gases through the stove, and the more heat retained for transfer to the room. The goal is to slow gases as much as possible

while maintaining adequate draft, so that gas temperature drops from around 900°C (1,652°F) in the firebox to about 150°C (302°F) in the chimney.

Two other construction rules regarding smoke channels are: (1) make horizontal channels 15 percent oversized to allow for accumulation of fly ash, so that it does not restrict the passage; (2) the smoke channel cross-section should increase by as much as 25 percent at major turns to avoid restricting gas flow.

In Austria, it is calculated that gases will cool down by 4° to 8°C (7.2° to 14.4°F) per meter as they rise within the chimney, the difference depending on how the chimney is built. If gases enter a chimney at 150°C (302°F) and rise ten meters, they lose perhaps 80°C (144°F) and emerge from the chimney at 70°C (158°F). This is looked upon as a safe level. Some stove builders will try for a little higher efficiency and bring gases into the chimney at 120°C (248°F); others try for less and come into the flue at 200°C (392°F).

In the typical five-channel Swedish stove, smoke passages are not tapered. They are uniform, about seventeen by seventeen centimeters. However, the first rising channel above the firebox is enlarged to accommodate the hottest gases. At the top of this first rising channel, the smoke passage divides into two seventeen-by-seventeen descending channels. The cross-section then remains the same until the chimney.

Inside any masonry stove, *it is important that smoke channels be smoothed and the corners rounded. Direction changes should be gradual and not abrupt.* The idea is to ease the flow of gases, to avoid sharp turns and rough surfaces. Above all, avoid dead-end tunnels where gases can collect and, if ignited, cause an explosion that could possibly damage the stove.

Chimneys

Recently I saw a terminal error in masonry stove design: a massive chimney located right on top of a brick stove.

In addition to the usual stresses, the stove thus had tons of masonry bearing down on it from above. This wasn't the worst of it. The design was weak, the materials poor; the stove began to come apart.

Properly built, a masonry stove can be torn down and rebuilt of the same materials without touching the chimney. In this case $8,000 worth of masonry had to come down to get at the stove. *Never build the chimney on top of the stove.*

Channel shape is significant too. Round channels provide better gas flow but are seldom used because they are less convenient for providing even transfer of heat to the flat surface of the stove. Square channels are second best; rectangular channels offer the poorest flow (which does not mean flow is so poor they are not used). The further the rectangle retreats from the square, the greater the resistance to gas flow.

One more aspect of smoke-channel design needs discussion, the question of vertical and horizontal channels. As you know by now, there are design differences here between central Europe and the lands to the north and east. Central Europe favors horizontal smoke channels. Finland, Russia, Sweden, and others favor the vertical run. Favors is perhaps too weak a word. A Finnish stove expert will look you in the eye and, with a patient smile, say "Smoke wants to go up. That's the natural thing. So we let it go up." About the fact that Finnish, Russian, or Swedish stoves next require the smoke to go down an equal distance, the expert may be silent. A Lithuanian writer, Leonidas Gimbutas, remarked in the 1920s that people in his country were switching to horizontal channel design because of greater fuel economy. It was difficult for me to see why this should necessarily be so. Marcus Bull's tests in the 1820s did show some slight improvement in efficiency from horizontal runs as against vertical runs, but the difference was so small it might well have been the result of extraneous factors not now evident.

I asked Gustav Jung for enlightenment, since he has spent a lifetime building stoves. He is also a rare stove builder in that he is familiar not only with his own country's tile-stove building tradition, but also with that of Russia. The choice, he felt, depended primarily on the chosen shape of the stove and on the dynamics (drawing power) of the chimney. If you have long vertical channels, some of them must go down as well as up. It takes more drawing power in the chimney to haul gases through a downward run than it does on a vertical or horizontal run. It can be done—it is done—but it takes more draft. Neither the vertical nor the horizontal smoke run is necessarily more efficient as to fuel consumption. Either can be efficient if well designed. Basically, horizontal or very gently rising smoke channels are used in central Europe for wood burning; they require less chimney power to make them work well. Mr. Jung feels that there will be greater soot or fly ash buildup where down-channels join up-channels in a vertical-mode stove. In Austria the stoves with vertical channels are those for coal or coke, where fly ash and soot are not a problem. Mr. Jung's is the best discussion I have come across on the vertical/horizontal channel question, and to me it makes sense.

DAMPERS

Swedish, Russian, Finnish, and east European stoves generally use dampers to close off the chimney flue entirely when the fire has burned out. Most brick stoves currently built in the U.S. follow the same practice. As mentioned before, in Germany, Austria, and Switzerland dampers that close the chimney entirely are forbidden by law, because of the danger that lethal gas may flow into the house when a damper is closed prematurely. The standard generally used in these countries is that dampers may not close more than 80 percent of the way; usually they are built so they close no more than two-thirds of the way. (See chapters 9 and 11 for further discussion.) I believe the Germans, Austrians and Swiss have it right: Build the stove with a damper that does not fully close. There are very real risks in full-closure dampers, which is why we do not use them with other heating devices, like iron stoves.

FUEL REQUIREMENT

Assume that in the hypothetical stove you want to get an output of four thousand kilocalories per hour for fourteen hours. How much wood do you need? Here is a handy formula.

$$\frac{R\ (4,000) \times T\ (14\ \text{hours})}{2,800} = \text{Wt. to (20 kg of wood)}$$

R stands for heating requirement in Kcal/hr

T stands for time in hours

Wt. stands for weight of wood fuel

2,800 is an assumed average fuel value of wood burned

TECHNIQUES FROM LITHUANIA

The following material comes from the book *Žemes Ŭkio Statyba* by Leonidas Gimbutas, Kauna, 1929. This was a text for builders. Relevant portions have been translated for me by the author's son, Dr. Jurgis Gimbutas, and I have summarized this material below, with occasional comments of my own in parentheses.

Three types of stoves are in use in Lithuania:

1. Stoves of large thermal mass, made of brick masonry covered with plaster or with tile.

2. Stoves of medium thermal mass, made of brick masonry in smaller volume and covered with sheet metal.

3. Stoves of small thermal mass, made of cast iron.

Each stove has two major parts: the firebox and the smoke passages. Firebox size depends on the type of fuel. The walls of the firebox must be firebrick and shall not transmit or conduct heat to the outside.

The stove should have an adequate surface area and an adequate thermal mass to hold heat for twenty-two hours. Heat dissipation should be even during that time even though the stove is fired only once a day. The required mass can be calculated approximately by the number of bricks; the brick will hold three calories after a firing. The standard brick size in Lithuania is 25 by 13 by 6.5 centimeters (somewhat larger than the standard American brick).

Within the stove are both vertical and horizontal smoke passages, whose cross-sectional area is a function of brick sizes, normally 12 by 12, or 12 by 25, or 20 by 20 centimeters. Chimney flues are normally 12 by 25 or 20 by 20 centimeters. Gases were expected to move through the passages within the stove at 1.5 to 2.5 meters per second, and to have a temperature of 200° to 300°C (392° to 572°F) on reaching the chimney. (This suggests a somewhat lower efficiency than the central European designer attempts today, shooting for 120° to 150°C—248° to 302°F—on entering the chimney.)

STOVE FOUNDATIONS

Foundations for stoves of large mass are built of stone or brick masonry directly on firm soil, independently of the building foundations, according to Leonidas Gimbutas. Stove foundation walls may be as much as forty centimeters (about sixteen inches) thick with a masonry arch on top. Over that two layers of brick will support the stove above.

Foundations for stoves on upper floors are made of special beams incorporated into the upper floor framing. For example three steel beams ten to twenty centimeters deep may be anchored into a masonry wall with planking six centi-meters thick to support the stove. Over this planking there should be two layers of brick. For further fire protection, a layer of felt impregnated with wet clay may be placed between the planking and the bricks above. Stoves without a grate or an ash pit should have better insulation over wood flooring. For these, two additional layers of brick (making four in all) with air spaces should provide adequate insulation from the heat of the hearth.

CONSTRUCTION OF STOVES OF LARGE THERMAL MASS

Typically stoves of large thermal mass are built of brick with tile or plaster covering the outer surface. Because of the low heat conductivity of brick, the stove will not transmit heat to the room until two or three hours after firing. It takes approximately twenty-four hours to transmit the heat from one firing.

The simplest type of large thermal mass stove is known in Lithuania as a Dutch stove, with vertical flues.

Typical dimensions for this stove would be:

Firebox: 25 to 38 centimeters wide, 38 to 50 centimeters long, 50 to 60 centimeters high.

Firebox walls: 25 centimeters thick, including brick plus tile.

Stove walls: 12 centimeters thick, plus any tile or plaster added.

Figure 176 Masonry stoves require adequate foundations to support their weight, as did these stone beehive houses from the Isle of Lewis off western Scotland. The beehive houses were in effect stoves that people lived in, like the black houses mentioned in chapter 2. Climate-tempering walls of turf and stone could be several feet thick. Fire burned on the floor.

Smoke passages: four to eight vertical flues, each 1.8 to 2.5 meters long. Total smoke passage length should not exceed 30 meters.

Leonidas Gimbutas quotes a Professor Lukaševičius to the effect that the simplest Dutch stoves had an efficiency of 35 percent without a grate, and of 50 percent with a grate. (Because the flue length is adequate to extract most of the heat from the gases before they reach the chimney, the obvious question is, Why such low efficiency? It is not clear from the text, but the answer must lie in air movement through the stove, carrying off heat from the brick before it can migrate through the stove wall to warm the dwelling.)

The professor improved efficiency by designing a double door (presumably tighter). He also put a mica window in the door. This made it possible to check progress of the fire without opening the door and letting a flood of cold air into the firebox, to carry warmth up the chimney. Prof. Lukaševičius changed the firebox design, sloping the sides at a 50° to 60° angle downward toward the narrow grate lying above an ash pit. In addition he altered the pattern of the smoke passages. The old pattern had the smoke traveling up and down repeatedly before reaching the chimney. In the new pattern the smoke rose in one passage from the firebox, then moved at the top of the stove into two or three downward passages, simultaneously. At the bottom of the stove was a distribution box. The several downward passages funneled smoke into this distribution box, and from there it made its way into the chimney. (The pattern was in this way very similar to the contraflow pattern used in Finland and Russia and now starting to make its way in the U.S. The

contraflow approach makes a more even heat distribution over the surface of this type of stove.)

Mortar for Lithuanian stove construction is made of rich "fat" clay cleaned of organic matter and mixed with an equal amount of fine quartz sand. On the top of the stove there should be two to three layers of brick. There should also be 40-centimeter clearance between the stove top and ceiling. Brick-stove clearances should be 6.5 to 12 centimeters from masonry walls and 40 centimeters from wooden walls. Fuels used in these Lithuanian stoves, aside from wood, included peat and coal. A grate is necessary for either peat or coal.

BRICK SIZES

National variations in brick size must be taken into account in considering some of the stove plans in this book. The old standard American brick was four by eight inches. A mason friend tells me this has now diminished to something that runs about 3⅝ by 7⅝ by 2¼ inches. Finnish and Russian bricks are much larger.

Finnish standard brick: 27 by 13 by 7.5 centimeters, or 10⅝ by 5¼ by 3 inches.

Finnish chimney brick: 25.7 by 12.3 by 5.7 centimeters, or 10¼ by 4⅞ by 2¼ inches.

Russian brick: 25 by 12 by 6.5 centimeters, or 9⅞ by 4¾ by 2 ⁹⁄₁₆ inches.

Appendix

1

Conversion Table

In working with both metric and U.S. measurements, the following equivalents may prove useful.

1 meter (m) = 3.281 ft or 39.37 in

1 centimeter (cm) = .3937 in

1 square meter (m^2) = 10.7639 ft^2 or 1550 in^2

1 cubic meter (m^3) = 35.31 ft^3 or 61023 in^3

1 kilogram (kg) = 2.2 lb

1 kilocalorie (kcal) = 3.968 Btu (British thermal units)

1 $kcal/m^2/hr$ = 0.369 $Btu/ft^2/hr$

1 $watt/m^2$ = 0.318 $Btu/ft^2/hr$

1 $kcal/hr/m^2/°C$ = 0.205 $Btu/hr/ft^2/°F$

1 $watt/m^2/°C$ = 0.176 $Btu/hr/ft^2/°F$

$°C = \frac{5}{9} \times °F - 32$

$°F = \frac{9}{5} \times °C + 32$

$1°C = 1.8°F$

$1°F = 0.556°C$

1 Btu = 252 calories = .252 kilocalories

Information Sources

North America

Information sources for North America are scattered. But they are increasing in number and sophistication. My own company, Heating Research Co., imports and sells antique cast iron stoves from Europe. We are experimenting in masonry stove design and as demand develops expect to supply assorted hardware and materials useful for construction: fuel doors, oven doors, iron fireboxes, ranges designed to be built into masonry central chimneys, grates, ash doors, cleanout doors, and so on. We are also considering supplying various refractory materials and mortars. Contact us for information. We are interested in contacting masons and builders with experience or interest in masonry stove construction, so that we can refer local inquiries to them.

Heating Research Co.
Acworth Road
Acworth, NH 03601
603–835–6109

There are many sources of materials in the U.S. suitable for masonry stove construction.

The Yellow Pages or Thomas' Register will disclose masonry supply, refractory companies, and decorative tile firms near you. Local industrial supply firms usually carry refractory products to sell to masons who do boiler and furnace repairs. Potters often have valuable information from their kiln-building experience. (See the three kiln books noted in chap. 13.) The most difficult items to locate are suitable doors and dampers or related hardware. Many present builders adapt airtight cast-iron stove doors and have dampers specially made.

I've found two major refractory firms especially helpful. Both make castable refractories, firebrick, and high-temperature mortars. Each produces a catalog that is an education in itself. The names of additional refractory firms can be found in *Thomas' Register.*

General Refractories Co.
U.S. Refractories Division
600 Grant St., Rm. 3000
Pittsburgh, PA 05219

A.P. Green Refractories Co.
Mexico, MO 65265

In high temperature situations, calcium aluminate cement should be used instead of the Portland variety. This can provide an alternative to the often more-expensive products of the refractory companies. A company whose refractory cements are widely available is:

Lehigh Portland Cement Co.
718 Hamilton Mall
Allentown, PA 18105

In Austria and Germany in the past potters made stove tiles, then designed and built stoves with them. Today people with all three skills are rare, but there is one source at least in the U.S.

Sigrid Scherm-Pratt
The Newfane Pottery
Box 10A
Newfane, VT 05345

Several companies in the U.S. and at least one in Canada currently offer tile stoves of one kind or another. These include:

Bow and Arrow Stove Co.
11 Hurley St.
Cambridge, MA 02141

Ka-Heat Kachelofen Ltd.
255 Delaware Ave.
Buffalo, NY 14202

Home Comfort Warming Center
2505 A Middle Country Rd.
Centereach NY 11720

Fundamental Energies, Inc.
16 Cumberland St.
Yarmouth, ME 04096

Alber's Inc.
976 Route 22
Bridgewater, NJ 08807

Ka-Heat Kachelofen Ltd.
P.O. Box 669
Cobourg, Ontario K9A 4R5
Canada

HDI Importers
85 Mechanic St.
Lebanon, NH 03766

Ronald Propst
800 West End Blvd.
Winston-Salem, NC 27101

Rotera Stoves
HWM Sales
208 W. State St.
Kennett Square, PA 19348

Ceramic Radiant Heat
5 Pleasant Drive
Lochmere, NH 03252

Starting in the northeast and now spreading into other regions, an increasing number of masons have begun experimenting with brick stoves. Word of their work spreads like ripples on a pond. Basilio Lepuschenko is one of the pioneers in the field. So is Albie Barden of Maine Wood Heat Co. Lepuschenko offers plans for a type of brick stove long used in east Europe. Maine Wood Heat Co. offers plans, workshops on stove construction, and hardware, such as stove doors, dampers, and even Finnish mortar.

Basilio Lepuschenko
RFD #1, Box 589
Richmond, ME 04357

Maine Wood Heat Co.
RFD 1, Box 38
Norridgewok, ME 04957

The builder of the $2,200 stove mentioned at the end of chapter 5, the one that heats 1,800 square feet on six cords of pine per year, is Fred Fitzpatrick of

Masonry Woodstoves, Inc.
Hoyts Wharf Road
Groton, MA 01450

Karoly Szoke, Jr. has a background in the construction of high-temperature furnaces used for glass-making and similar uses. He has designed and built a large masonry cooking/heating center, intended to supply all heat for dwellings up to 2,800 square feet. Plans are available from:

Szoke Construction Co., Inc.
1844 Merrill St.
Lincoln Park, MI 48146

One firm in the U.S. has begun producing refractory concrete block components for a heat-storage fireplace. (See fig. 163). Other products, including heat-storage stoves, are in design stages. This approach offers exciting prospects for low-cost heat storage.

Thermal Energy Storage Systems Inc.
Box M, Mine Road
Kenvil, NJ 07847

There are at least three organizations, two in the U.S. and one in Canada, which can be helpful with general masonry questions. One of these, the Brick Institute of America, has published fireplace, chimney and masonry stove plans.

Brick Institute of America
1750 Old Meadow Road
McLean, VA 22101

International Masonry Institute.
823 Fifteenth St. N.W.
Washington, D.C. 20005

Centre for Research and Development in
   Masonry
105–4528 6A St. N.E.
Calgary, Alberta, Canada T2E 4B2

A complete listing of European suppliers and stove builders would be long and probably soon out of date. So instead I've listed central information sources for major countries. These can offer current lists of builders, suppliers, etc.

Austria

Verband der Kachelindustrie und der
    Hafner-Heizungsbauer Osterreichs sowie
    der Zulieferfirmen
Paltramplatz 7
Vienna, Austria

Sommerhuber
Pachergasse 19
A–4400 Steyr, Austria

This is an outstanding tile maker and stove
design firm.

Federal Republic of Germany

Informationsstelle Kachelofen
Postfach 80 05 01
7000 Stuttgart 80
Federal Republic of Germany

Finland

Building Information Institute
(Rakennustietoosäätiö)
Lonnrotinkatu 20 B
SF–00120 Helsinki 12, Finland

Suomen Tiiliteollisuusliitto R.Y.
Iso Roobertinkatu 20
00120 Helsinki 12, Finland

Netherlands

De Twaalf Ambachten
Esschebaan 9A
5282 JK Boxtel
Netherlands

Switzerland

Verband Schweizerischer
    Kachelofenfabrikanten
Obstgartenstrasse 28
8035 Zurich, Switzerland

Sweden

New tile stoves are no longer produced in
Sweden, nor is there a central information
source. The remaining tile-stove builders
confine themselves to restoring and rebuild-
ing antiques. Björn-Erik Lindblom is knowledgeable about the world of antique Swedish
tile stoves, and has agreed to act as guide for
those interested in them.

Björn-Erik Lindblom
Bockhornsgatan 11c
S–413 17 Gothenburg, Sweden

Interior Flue Design Details

The illustrations on the following pages will be useful to those who wish a more detailed picture of interior flue design in European masonry stoves. The dimensions of Finnish and Russian bricks can be found in chapter 13. These dimensions are essential in interpreting the true size of the stoves shown here; American bricks are smaller than those of either Finland or Russia.

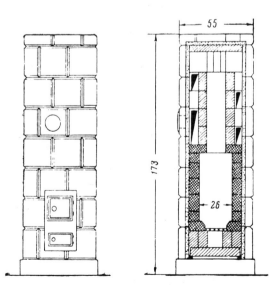
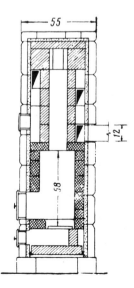

Figure 177 The Russians have also experimented with heat-storage stoves made from refractory concrete. This example is a small Russian stove built from specially formed concrete blocks. It is approximately twenty-two inches square and sixty-eight inches high. The dimensions given in the drawing are in centimeters. Drawing from L. A. Semenov, courtesy of the Copyright Agency of the U.S.S.R.

168

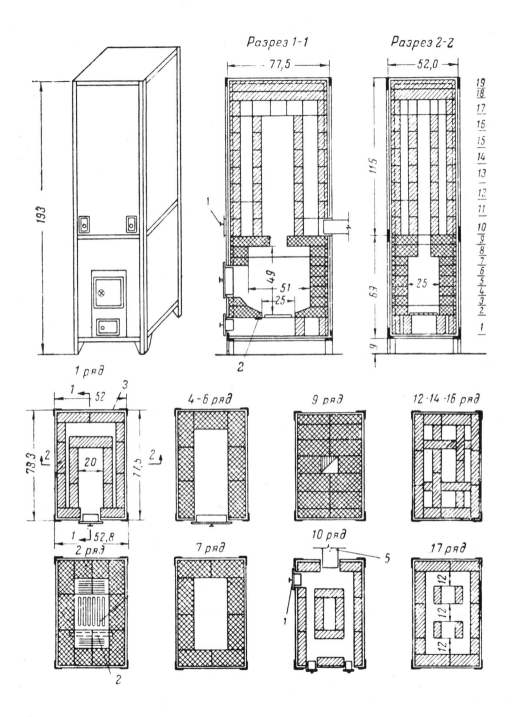

Figure 178 This is a brick stove set into a steel frame and enclosed in sheet metal, from the U.S.S.R. Similar stoves have been produced in Finland and elsewhere. The technique provided an economical means of producing heat-storage stoves of modest size, and the Finnish writer G.E. Asp thought highly of their performance. Drawing from L.A. Semenov, courtesy of the Copyright Agency of the U.S.S.R.

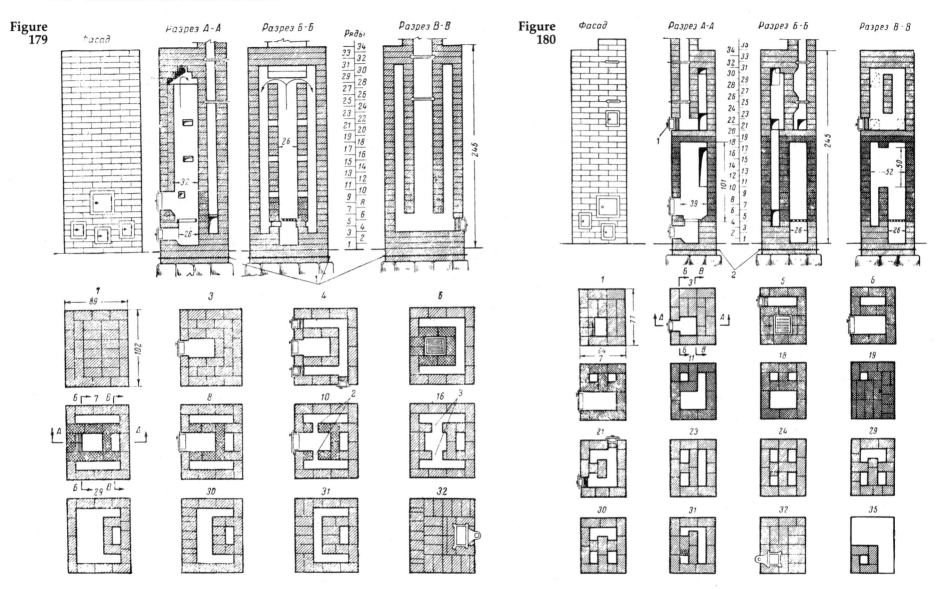

Figure 179

Фасад Разрез А-А Разрез Б-Б Ряды Разрез В-В

Figure 180

Фасад Разрез А-А Разрез Б-Б Разрез В-В

Figures 179 (left), **180** (right), **181** (facing page top), **182** (facing page bottom) These four stoves are brick models from the U.S.S.R. They illustrate some of the many possible variations that have been tried in vertical smoke channel design. Note that each course of bricks on these stove plans is numbered; also that each of the smaller horizontal cross-sections has the course number above it, to show the level at which the section is taken. For example, in figure 179, which shows a Russian version of the contra-flow stove, the section taken at course level four shows three cleanout doors for the smoke channels plus a (larger) ash cleanout

Figure 181

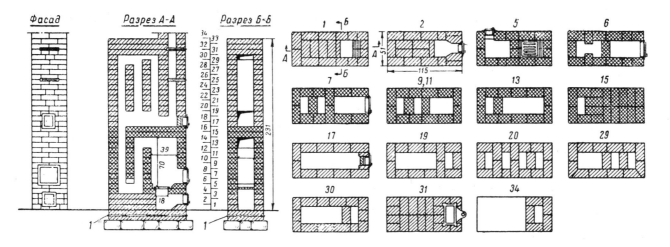

Figure 182

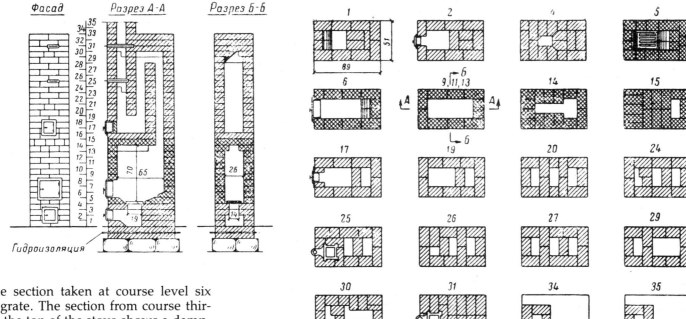

door. The section taken at course level six shows a grate. The section from course thirty-two at the top of the stove shows a damper closing off the channel leading into the chimney. (Each of the four stoves has two complete-closure dampers.) The illustrations in figures 177 through 182 are from the book *Teploustojchivost i pechnoe otoplenie zhilykh i obschestvennykh zdanij,* by L. A. Semenov, published in Moscow in 1950. Courtesy of the Copyright Agency of the U.S.S.R.

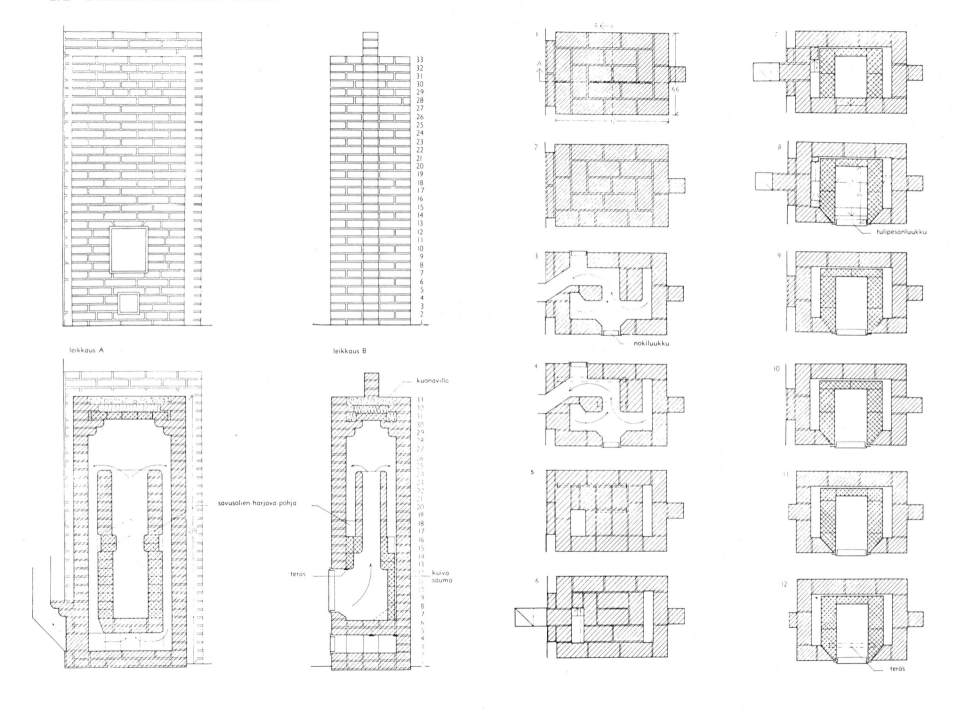

leikkaus A

leikkaus B

kuonavilla

savusolien harjava pohja

teras

kuiva sauma

tulipesanluukku

nokiluukku

teras

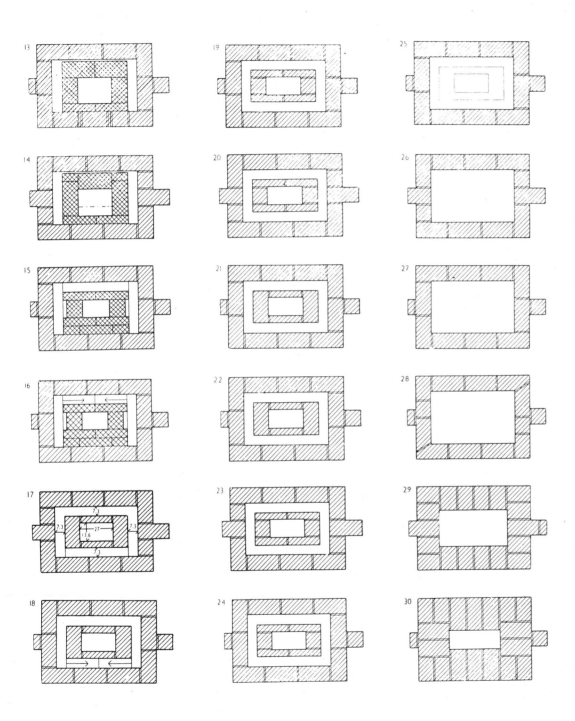
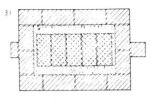
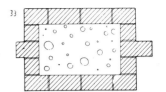
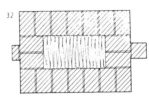

Figure 183 The design for this brick contra-flow stove originated in Sweden, though it has been more widely used in the U.S.S.R. and Finland. Recent research in Finland has been directed at upgrading the design, particularly firebox conformation. The stove's name is derived from the fact that warm room air rises along the outer surface of the stove, while in the smoke channels just inside hot gases from the firebox are passing downward. One advantage of the design, according to those who have used it in Finland, is the comparatively even heating of the stove's outer surface. Another advantage is that the centrally located firebox "floats;" that is, the firebox is structurally separate from the outer shell of the stove. The stress effect of the firebox's greater expansion during firing is thus isolated. Smoke from the fire rises through a single central channel to the top of the stove. There it divides and passes downward through two separate channels to the bottom of the stove. The smoke then moves a short distance horizontally, and rises through a single channel toward the chimney. Maine Wood Heat Co. (see Information Sources) has been active in constructing and promoting this design in the U.S., and has plans available. Drawings courtesy of Rakennustietosäätiö, Helsinki.

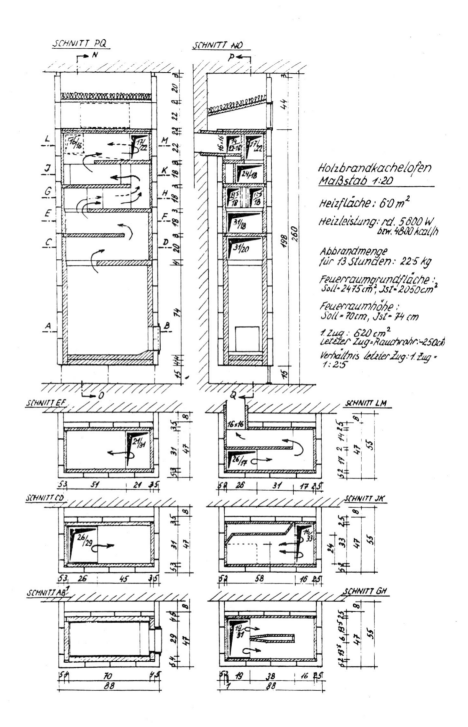

Figure 184 This tile stove design is fairly typical for Germany and Austria. Note at upper left the gas slot (*gasschlitz*) through which any accumulated gases can escape upward from the top of the first downward channel beyond the firebox. Note also the small size of the final smoke channel, only fifteen by fifteen centimeters, at the point where the channel runs into the chimney flue. (See section, or *schnitt*, GH.) All dimensions are in centimeters. Stove surface area is 5.75 square meters. Courtesy of *Informationsstelle Kachelofen*, Stuttgart.

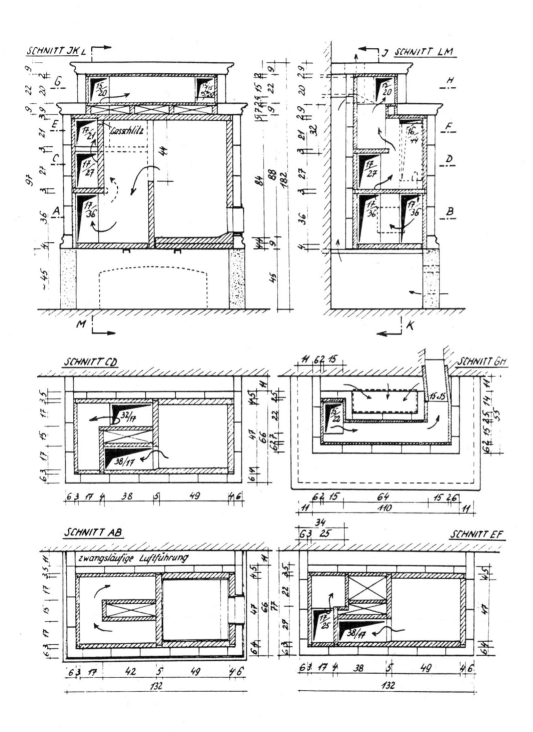

Figure 185 This tile stove has a surface area of six square meters and an all-horizontal smoke channel plan. Note how the cross-section of the smoke channels shrinks between the firebox and the chimney. The first channel (see section, or *schnitt*, CD) is twenty-six by twenty-nine centimeters; the flue opening (section LM) is sixteen by sixteen centimeters. All dimensions in centimeters. Courtesy of *Informationsstelle Kachelofen*, Stuttgart.

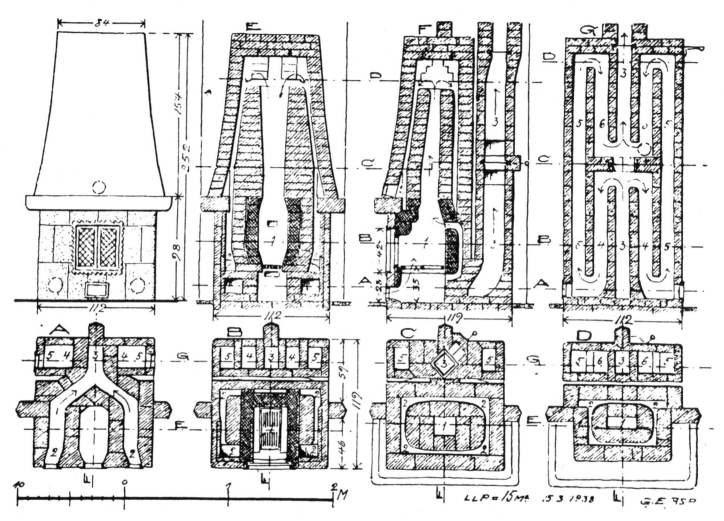

Figure 186 The main body of this Finnish stove is built in contraflow style, like the model shown in figure 183. But note the large fuel doors shown here. If opened, these doors in effect turn the stove into a fireplace. The difficulty is, when the big doors are open a great volume of air moves through the smoke channels, much more than when the stove is used in the closed-door mode. This volume of air fans the fire; it also moves heat more swiftly through the smoke channels and up the chimney; efficiency falls. To compensate, the designer has added an extra heat-storage battery behind the main body of the contraflow stove. The smoke moves through this battery after leaving the contraflow section, giving up heat that would otherwise be lost up the chimney. The intent of this design is to make possible an efficient masonry stove/fireplace combination. To trace the smoke path through this rather complex system, follow the numbers within the smoke channels in order. No. 1 indicates the firebox and No. 2 the descending smoke channels of the contraflow section. Nos. 3, 4, and 5 indicate the channels of the battery section. Drawing by G. E. Asp, from his book, *Uuninmuuraaja*, courtesy of Otava.

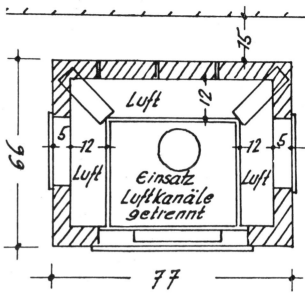

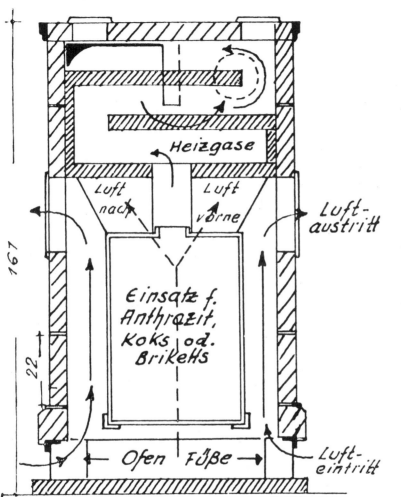

Figure 187 The use of a cast-iron firebox *(einsatz)* in a masonry stove is common practice today in Austria and Germany. In the example illustrated here, smoke passes through an abbreviated channel system after it leaves the iron firebox. Today, however, an iron heat exchanger is often used in place of the abbreviated channel system. Stoves of this type are really hybrids, combining the fast response of the iron stove with a measure of the heat storage capacity of all-masonry stoves. The outer and visible portion of the stove is commonly tile, though it may also be brick; the iron firebox remains hidden inside the masonry. In part these stoves resemble the circulator stoves used in North America. Cool room air moves through grates placed at floor level in the tile or brick facade of the stove. (See arrow labeled *luft eintritt.)* This air warms on the side of the cast iron firebox, rises, and then exits through another grate. (See arrow labeled *luft austritt.)* So the stove heats by convection as well as by radiation from the masonry. Frequently the iron firebox is placed so that the fuel door is accessible from one room, while the stove itself is in the adjoining room. Dimensions in centimeters. Drawing from *Kachelofen und Kamin,* by Hans Grohmann, Verlag Georg D. W. Callwey, Munich, 1951.

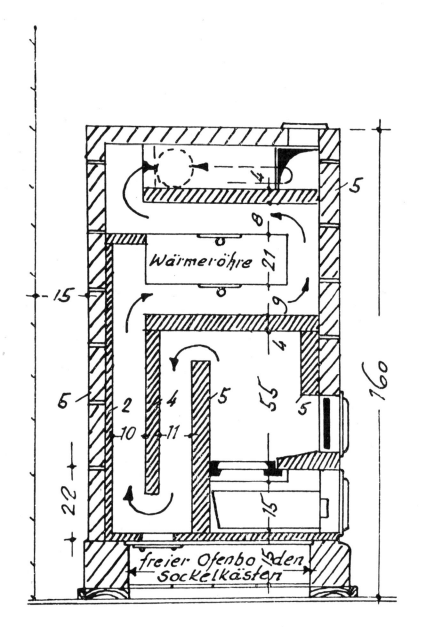

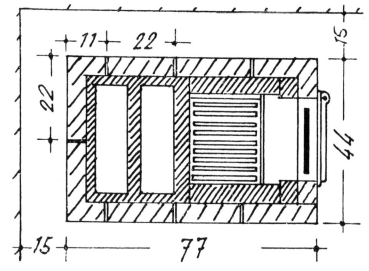

Figure 188   The smoke-channel pattern in this stove has been a common one in places like Austria and Germany. Note the small oven (*wärmeröhre*) built in just above the firebox. The smoke channels run the full width of this stove except at the top level, where channel width is cut in half. The smoke travels from the back to the front of the stove through one of these half-width channels, and then back to the smoke pipe opening (dotted circle) through the other. Dimensions are in centimeters. Drawing from *Kachelofen und Kamin*, by Hans Grohmann, Verlag Georg D. W. Callwey, Munich, 1951.

Bibliography

This bibliography, already long, is incomplete. I have left out most American references on wood burning. These are readily available in work by Jay Shelton and in the excellent bibliography prepared by Bill Day. I have tried to include many European references not readily available in wood-burning bibliographies. Here again the list is incomplete. The reader who wishes to go further in research should consult bibliographies in the works listed below.

Writers whose work I have found especially helpful in preparing this book include: Robert Meikelham (writing as Walter Bernan), W. Hausler, Alfred Faber, Catherine Perlès, Kenneth Oakley, Arne Nygard-Nilssen, Sigurd Erixon, K. Kwasniewski, Theodore A. Wertime, barons Cronstedt and Wrede, Peter Michelsen, I. S. Podgorodnikov, L. A. Semenov, and (on the hypocaust) F. Kretzschmer, D. Baatz, and T. Rook.

Acerbi, Giuseppe. *Travels Through Sweden, Finland, and Lapland to the North Cape, 1798–99.* London, 1802.

Ambrosiani, Sune. "Till Eldstadens Historia" from *Meddelanden fran Svenska Slojdforeningen.* Stockholm, 1904.

Asp, G.E. *Uuninmuuraaja.* Otava, Helsinki, 1944.

Baatz, Dietwulf. "Das Badegebaude Des Limeskastells Walldurn." *Saalburg-Jahrbuch,* Vol. 35. 1978.

_____"Heizversuch An Einer Rekonstruierten Kanalheizung in der Saalburg." *Saalburg-Jahrbuch,* Vol. 36. 1979.

Balassa, Ivan, and Gyula Ortutay. *Magyar Néprajz.* Corvina, Budapest, 1979.

Batky, Zsigmond. "Magyar tuzhelyek es haztipusok." *Néprajzi Értesitö,* Budapest, 1930.

Baur-Heinhold, Margarete. *Deutsche Bauernstuben.* Karl Robert Langewiesche Nachfolger Hans Koster, Konigstein im Taunus, 1975.

Benet, Sula, ed. and trans. *The Village of Viriatino.* Doubleday, New York, 1970.

Bennett, H.S. *Life on the English Manor.* Cambridge University Press, London, 1974.

_____*The Pastons and Their England.* Cambridge University Press, London, 1970.

Bernan, Walter (Robert Meikelham). *On the History and Art of Warming and Ventilating Rooms and Buildings,* Vols. I and II. George Bell, London, 1845.

Biringuccio, Vannoccio. *The Pirotechnia,* trans. from the Italian edition of 1540 by C.S. Smith and M.T. Gnudi. The American Institute of Mining and Metallurgical Engineers, New York, 1943.

Black Elk. *The Sacred Pipe,* Joseph Epes Brown, ed. University of Oklahoma Press, Norman, Okla., 1953.

Boon, George C. *Silchester: The Roman Town of Calleva.* David and Charles, London, 1974.

Booz, Allen, and Hamilton, Inc. *Assessment of Proposed Federal Tax Credits for Residential Wood Burning Equipment* (draft). Prepared for U.S. Department of Energy, Mar. 21, 1979.

Bradburd, R.M. *The Use of Wood for Fuel, Historical Series and Projection to the Year 2,000.* Paper prepared for the U.S. Department of Energy, 1979.

Braudel, Fernand. *The Mediterranean and the Mediterranean World in the Age of Philip II.* William Collins Sons & Co. Ltd. and Harper and Row, London and New York, 1976.

———*The Structures of Everyday Life,* Vol. I. English trans. copyright 1981 by William Collins Sons & Co. Ltd. and Harper & Row, London and New York.

Brown, F.L. *Theories of the Combustion of Wood and its Control.* Forest Products Laboratory, (USDA) Report No. 2136, Dec., 1958.

Bryson, Reid A., and Thomas J. Murray. *Climates of Hunger.* University of Wisconsin Press, Madison, Wisc., 1977.

Bugge, Gunnar, and Christian Norberg-Schulz. *Stav og Laft.* Norske Arkitekters Landsforbunds, Oslo, 1969.

Bull, Marcus. *Experiments to Determine the Comparative Quantities of Heat Evolved in the Combustion of the Principal Varieties of Wood and Coal Used in the U.S. for Fuel.* Transactions of the American Philosophical Society, III (new series), Philadelphia, 1830.

Burnham, R.E. *Who Are the Finns?* Faber and Faber, Ltd., London, 1946.

Caldwell, Jos. R., ed. *Investigations at Tal-i-Iblis.* Illinois State Museum, Springfield, Ill., 1967.

Campbell, Joseph. *The Masks of God: Primitive Mythology.* The Viking Press, New York, 1970.

Carcopino, Jerome. *Daily Life in Ancient Rome.* Yale University Press, New Haven, 1940.

Childe, V. Gordon. *The Dawn of European Civilization.* Routledge and Kegan Paul, Ltd., London, 1957.

———*Skara Brae.* Kegan Paul, Trench, Trubner & Co., London, 1931.

Clark, Grahame. *The Earlier Stone Age Settlement of Scandinavia.* Cambridge University Press, London, 1975.

Cline, Walter. *Mining and Metallurgy in Negro Africa.* George Banta Pub. Co., Menasha, Wisc., 1937.

Condominas, Georges. *We Have Eaten the Forest.* Hillard Wang, a division of Farrar, Straus and Giroux, New York, 1977.

Coxwell, C. Fillingham. *Siberian and Other Folk Tales.* C.W. Daniel Co., London, 1925.

Cronstedt, Baron Johan, and Gen. Fabian Wrede. *Samling af Beskrifningar pa Atskilliga Eldstader, Inrattade til Besparing af Wede.* Stockholm, 1775.

Davidson, Thomas. "The Needfire Ritual." *Antiquity,* Sept., 1955.

Day, Bill. *Wood Stove Durability: A Literature Review.* Western Solar Utilization Network, Portland, Oreg., 1980.

Deffontaines, Pierre. *L'homme et sa maison.* Gallimard, Paris, 1972.

Dick, Everett. *The Sod House Frontier, 1854–1890.* University of Nebraska Press, Lincoln, 1979.

Duby, Georges. *The Early Growth of the European Economy.* Cornell University Press, Ithaca, N.Y., 1974.

Dupree, Louis. *Afghanistan.* Princeton University Press, Princeton, N.J., 1973.

Eckholm, Erik P. *The Other Energy Crisis: Firewood.* Worldwatch Institute, Washington, D.C., 1975.

Edgerton, Samuel Y., Jr. "Heating Stoves in Eighteenth Century Philadelphia." *The Bulletin of the Association for Preservation Technology,* Vol. III., Nos. 2–3. Ottawa, 1971.

———"The Myth of the Franklin Stove." *Early American Life,* June, 1976.

Edlin, Herbert L. *Woodland Crafts in Britain.* David & Charles, Newton Abbott, 1974.

Eliade, Mircea. *Rites and Symbols of Initiation.* Harper and Row, New York, 1965.

Ercker, Lazarus. *Treatise on Ores and Assaying,* trans. from German edition of 1580 by A.G. Sisco and C.S. Smith. Copyright 1951 by the University of Chicago Press.

Erixon, Sigurd. "Eldhus." *Svenska Kulturbilder,* Stockholm, 1937.

———"Spjallet, en Exponent for Svensk Bostadsteknik." *Svenska Kulturbilder,* Stockholm, 1937.

Evans, E. Estyn. *Irish Folk Ways*. Routledge and Kegan Paul Ltd., London, 1957.

Faber, Alfred. "1000 Jahre Werdegang von Herd und Ofen." *Abhandlungen und Berichte*, Vol. 18. Deutsches Museum, Munich, 1950.

Fabre, J.Henri. *The Life of the Fly*. Dodd, Mead & Co., New York, 1925.

Fathy, Hassan. *Architecture for the Poor*. University of Chicago Press, 1973.

Forbes, R.J. *Studies in Ancient Technology*, Vol. VI. E.J. Brill, Leiden, 1966.

Franz, Rosemarie. *Der Kachelofen*. Akademische Druck-u., Verlagsanstalt, Graz, 1969.

Frayn, Joan M. *Subsistence Farming in Roman Italy*. Centaur Press Ltd., London, 1979.

Frazier, Sir James G. *The Golden Bough*. Macmillan Publishing Co., New York, 1978.

Garrison, F.H. "The History of Heating, Ventilation and Lighting." *Bulletin of the New York Academy of Medicine*, Vol. III. No. 2. New York, 1927.

Gebhard, Torsten. *Kachelöfen*. Verlag G.D.W. Callwey, Munich, 1981.

Gernet, Jacques. *Daily Life in China on the Eve of the Mongol Invasion, 1250–1276*. George Allen and Unwin Ltd., London, 1962.

Gimbutas, Marija. *The Balts*. Thames and Hudson, London, 1963.

——*The Prehistory of Eastern Europe*. Peabody Museum, Harvard University, Cambridge, Mass., 1956.

——*The Slavs*. Thames and Hudson, London, 1971.

Gimpel, Jean. *The Medieval Machine*. Holt, Rinehart and Winston, New York, 1976.

Givoni, B. *Man, Climate and Architecture*. Applied Science Publishers Ltd., London, 1976.

Glesinger, Egon. *The Coming Age of Wood*. Simon and Schuster, Inc., New York, 1949.

Gourdin, W.H. and W.D. Kingery. "The Beginnings of Pyrotechnology; Neolithic and Egyptian Lime Plaster." *Journal of Field Archaeology*, Vol. 2., Nos. 1/2. 1975.

Gowlett, J.A.J.; J.W.K. Harris; D. Walton; and B.A. Wood. "Early archaeological sites, hominid remains and traces of fire from Chesowanja, Kenya." *Nature*, Vol. 294. Nov. 12, 1981.

Grant, I.F. *Highland Folk Ways*. Routledge and Kegan Paul Ltd., London, 1961.

Grohmann, Hans. *Kachelöfen und Kamin*. Verlag Georg D.W. Callwey, Munich, 1951.

Grützmacher, Bernd. *Kachelofenbau*. Verlag G.D.W. Callwey, Munich, 1981.

Gschwend, Max. *Schweizer Bauernhauser*. Verlag Paul Haupt, Bern, 1971.

Habicht, Tamara. *Eesti Saun*. Valgus, Tallinn, 1972.

Harrison. H.S. "Firemaking, Fuel and Lightning" in *A History of Technology*, edited by Chas. Singer, E.J. Holmyard, and A.R. Hall. Oxford University Press, Oxford, 1954.

Hausler, W. *Technisches Handbuch des Hausbrandes*. Vereinigung Kantonal-Schweizerischer Feuerversicherungsanstalten, Bern, 1950.

Havard, Henry. *Dictionnaire de l'ameublement et de la décoration depuis le XIII siècle*. Maison Quantin, Paris, 1887–90.

Hebgen, Heinrich. *Ratgeber Kachelofen*. Friedr. Vieweg & Sohn, Braunschweig, 1981.

Hickock, Henry W. "New and Old Techniques for Burning Wood." *Connecticut Woodlands*, Winter 1974. (Reprinted from the Cheshire, Ct., *Herald*.)

Hix, John. *The Glass House*. M.I.T. Press, Cambridge, Mass., 1974.

Hodges, Henry. "Roman Baths." *British History Illustrated*, Vol. I, No. 4. London, 1975.

——*Technology in the Ancient World*. Pelican Books, London, 1971.

Hodous, Lewis. *Folkways in China*. Arthur Probsthain, London, 1929.

Holt, Ivar. *Braendeovnen.* Clausen Bøger, Copenhagen, 1980.

Hommel, Rudolf P. *China at Work.* John Day Co., New York, 1937.

Hough, Walter. *Fire as an Agent in Human Culture.* Bulletin No. 139, The Smithsonian Institution, Washington, D.C., 1926.

Huber, Walther. "Hypokausten." *Saalburg-Jahrbuch,* Vol. 15. 1956.

Huser, Heribert. "Warmetechnische Messungen An Einer Hypokaustenheizung in der Saalburg." *Saalburg-Jahrbuch,* Vol. 36. 1979.

Hyytiainen, Heikki. *Muuratut tulisijat.* Rakennustietosäätiö, Helsinki, 1979.

Jackson, Wes. "Alternatives in Agriculture." *The Land Report,* No. 14, Fall 1981. The Land Institute, Salina, Kansas.

Johannsen, Ebbe. *Kakkelovn og jernovn.* Nyt Nordisk Forlag Arnold Busck A/S, Copenhagen, 1980.

Johns, Tom, and Tim Miller. *The Sauna Book.* Harper and Row, New York, 1977.

Kang, Younghill. *The Grass Roof.* Charles Scribner's Sons, New York and London, 1966.

Kauffman, Henry J. *The American Fireplace.* Galahad Books, New York, 1972.

Keep, William J. Unpublished original manuscript on the history of stoves, Baker Library, Harvard University, Cambridge, Mass., 1916.

Kim, Sang-sul. *Ondol Kaejoron.* Seoul, 1961.

Kiss, Lajos. "A boglyakemence és elete Hódmezövásárhelyen." *Ethnographia,* Budapest, 1953.

Klein, Richard G. *Ice-Age Hunters of the Ukraine.* University of Chicago Press, Chicago, 1973.

Klima, Bohuslav. "Coal in the Ice Age." *Antiquity,* June, 1956.

———"Palaeolithic Huts at Dolni Vestonice, Czechoslovakia." *Antiquity,* March, 1954.

Kopper, John S., and Guillermo Rossello-Bordoy. "Megalithic Quarrying Techniques and Limestone Technology in Eastern Spain." *Journal of Field Archaeology,* Vol. I. Nos. 1/2. 1975.

Kretzschmer, Fritz. "Die Heizung der Aula Palatina in Trier." *Germania,* Vol. 33. 1955.

———"Hypokausten." *Saalburg-Jahrbuch,* Vol. 12. 1953.

Kundzins, Pauls. *Latvju Sēta.* Daugava, Stockholm, 1974.

Kwasniewski, Krzyystof. *Paleniska i Piece w Polskim Budownictwie Ludowym.* Polish Academy of Sciences, Wroclaw-Warsaw-Krakow, 1963.

Laubin, Reginald and Gladys. *The Indian Tipi.* University of Oklahoma Press, Norman, Okla., 1957.

Laufer, Berthold. *Chinese Pottery of the Han Dynasty.* E.J. Brill, Leiden, 1909.

Leroi-Gourhan, A., and M. Brezillon. "Fouilles de Pincevent; Essai d'analyse ethnographique d'un habitat magdalenien." VII Suppl. to *Gallia Prehistoire,* Paris, CNRS, 1972.

Marschack, Alexander. *The Roots of Civilization.* Weidenfeld and Nicolson, London, 1972.

Maxwell, T.T.; Dyer, D.F.; et al. Research reports on wood burning by the Department of Mechanical Engineering, Auburn University, Auburn, Ala., 1979–1981.

McKay. A.G. *Houses, Villas and Palaces in the Roman World.* Cornell University Press, Ithaca, N.Y., 1975.

McKinnon, Gordon P. *Fire Protection Handbook.* 14th ed. National Fire Protection Association, Boston, 1976.

Mellaart, James. *Earliest Civilizations of the Near East.* Thames and Hudson, London, 1974.

Mercer, Henry C. *The Bible in Iron.* Bucks County Historical Society, Doylestown, Pa., 1961.

Michelsen, Peter. *Ildsteder og Opvarmning.* The National Museum, Copenhagen, 1968.

Mindeleff, Victor. *A Study of Pueblo Architecture, Tusayan and Cibola.* The Smithsonian Institution, Bureau of Ethnology, 8th Annual Report for 1886–1887, Washington, D.C., 1891.

Mitchell, Sir Arthur. *The Past in the Present.* Harper and Bros., New York, 1881.

Morse, Edward S. *Japanese Homes.* Ticknor and Co., Boston, 1886.

Mumford, Lewis. *The City in History.* Harcourt, Brace and World, New York, 1961.

Needham, Joseph. *Science and Civilization in China,* Part III, Vol. IV. Cambridge University Press, London, 1971.

Neuberger, Albert. *The Technical Arts and Sciences of the Ancients.* Macmillan, New York, 1930.

Nilsson, Axel. "Aril, spis och ugn." *Ymer,* 1905.

Northeastern Wood Utilization Council (various bulletins published at New Haven in the 1940s and 1950s).

Noyes, James O. *Roumania.* Rudd and Carleton, New York, 1857.

Nygard-Nilssen, Arne. *Norsk Jernskulptur.* J.W. Cappelens Forlag, Oslo, 1944.

Oakley, Kenneth. "The Earliest Firemakers." *Antiquity,* June, 1956.

———"On Man's Use of Fire." *Social Life of Early Man,* S.L. Washburn, ed. Aldine, Chicago, 1961.

Olin, S.C. *Sauna; The Way to Health.* Health Factor Books, New York Mills, Minn., 1963.

Paget, John. *Hungary and Transylvania.* Lee and Blanchard, Philadelphia, 1850.

Peate, Iorwerth C. *Tradition and Folk Life.* Faber and Faber, London, 1972.

Peirce, Josephine. *Fire on the Hearth; The Evolution and Romance of the Heating Stove.* Pond-Ekberg Co., Springfield, Mass., 1951.

Perlès, Catherine. "Hearth and Home in the Old Stone Age." *Natural History,* Vol. 90, No. 10. Oct., 1981.

———"Le Feu." *La Prehistoire Francais,* Vol. I. Paris, 1976.

———"L'homme et le feu." *Encyclopaedia Universalis,* mise à jouz, 1981.

———*Prehistoire du feu.* Masson, Paris, 1977.

Pfeiffer, John E. *The Emergence of Man.* Harper and Row, New York, 1969.

———"When Homo Erectus Tamed Fire, He Tamed Himself." *New York Times Magazine,* Dec. 11, 1966.

Phillips, E.D. *The Royal Hordes.* Thames and Hudson, London, 1965.

Piggott, Stuart. *Ancient Europe.* Edinburgh University Press, Edinburgh, 1965.

Podgorodnikov, I.S. *Russkaya Pech'.* Ministerstva Kommunalnogo Hozyastva, Moscow-Leningrad, 1950.

Pruitt, Ida. *A Daughter of Han.* Yale University Press, New Haven, Ct., 1945.

Rackham, Oliver. *Ancient Woodland.* Edward Arnold, London, 1980.

Lord Raglan. *The Temple and the House.* W.W.Norton, New York, 1964.

Rapoport, Amos. *House Form and Culture.* Prentice Hall, Englewood Cliffs, N.J., 1969.

Rees, Alwyn D. and Brinley. *Celtic Heritage.* Thames and Hudson, London, 1961.

Reineke, L.H. *Wood Fuel Combustion Practice.* Forest Products Laboratory, Forest Service, U.S. Dept. of Agriculture, Report No. 1666–18, May, 1961.

———*Wood Fuel Preparation.* U.S. Forest Research Note FPL–090, Jan., 1965.

Reynolds, Peter J. *Farming in the Iron Age.* Cambridge University Press, London, 1976.

Richards, D.H. "The Chimney." *Journal of the British Archaeological Association,* Vol. XIV. 1961.

Riché, Pierre. *Daily Life in the World of Charlemagne.* University of Pennsylvania Press, Philadelphia, 1978.

Rothenberg, Benno. *Timna.* London, 1972.

Rudofsky, Bernard. *The Prodigious Builders.* Harcourt Brace Jovanovich, New York, 1977.

Russell, Howard S. *A Long, Deep Furrow.* University Press of New England, Hanover, 1976.

Rye, Owen S., and Clifford Evans. *Traditional Pottery Techniques of Pakistan*. The Smithsonian Institution, Washington, D.C., 1976.

Sauer, Carl O. "The Agency of Man on Earth." *Man's Role in Changing the Face of the Earth*, W.L. Thomas, Jr., ed. University of Chicago Press, Chicago, 1956.

———"Sedentary and Mobile Bents in Early Societies." *Social Life of Early Man*, S.L. Washburn, ed. Aldine, Chicago, 1961.

Seeley, L.E., and F.W. Keaton. "Wood-burning Space Heaters." *Mechanical Engineering*, Dec., 1940.

Selling, Gosta. "Svenska 1700-Talskakelugnar." *Svenska Kulturbilder*, Stockholm, 1937.

Semenov, L.A. *Teploustojchivost' i Pechnoe Otoplenie Zhilykh i Obstchestvennykh Zdanij*. Ministerstva Stroitelstva Predpryatii Mashinostroenya, Moscow, 1950.

Shelton, Jay. "Steadiness and Control in Wood Heating Systems." *Wood Burning Quarterly*, Summer, 1977.

Shelton, Jay, and Andrew Shapiro. *The Woodburners Encyclopedia*. Vermont Crossroads Press, Waitsfield, Vt., 1976.

Shuffrey, L.A. *The English Fireplace*. B.T. Batsford, London, 1912.

Shurtleff, William. "How to Keep Warm for Pennies, Japanese Style." *Organic Gardening and Farming*, Mar., 1977.

Singer, Charles. with E.J. Holmyard and A.R. Hall. *A History of Technology*, Vol. I and Vol. II. Oxford University Press, Oxford, 1954.

Smith, Arthur H. *Chinese Characteristics*. Fleming H. Revell Co., New York, 1894.

———*Village Life in China*. Fleming H. Revell Co., New York, 1899.

Soeder, Hans. *Das Dorf Tritschuny im Litavisch*. (Dissertation) Berlin-Darmstadt, 1918.

Spencer, J.E. "The Houses of the Chinese." *The Geographical Review*, Vol. 37. 1947.

Svensk Uppslagsbok. 1950.

Thurner, Josef. *Offene Kamine und Kachelofen*. Pinguin-Verlag, Innsbruck, 1974.

Tillman, David A. *Wood as an Energy Resource*. Academic Press, New York, 1978.

Travis, William. *Interval on Symi*. Gambit, Inc., Boston, 1971.

Troyat, Henri. *Daily Life in Russia Under the Last Tsar*. George Allen and Unwin Ltd., London, 1961.

Tunander, Britt and Ingemar. *Kakelugnar*. ICA-Forlaget, Vasteras, 1976.

Undset, Sigrid. *Kristin Lavransdatter*. Alfred A. Knopf, New York, 1931.

Vahros, Igor. *Zur Geschichte und Folklore der Grossrussischen Sauna*. Suomalainen Tiedeakatemia, Helsinki, 1966.

Valonen, Nilo. *Zur Geschichte der Finnischen Wohnstuben*. Suomalais-Ugrilainen Seura, Helsinki, 1963.

Vastad, Kurt. "Nar Varmen Var en Kakelugn." *Hem och Fritid*, Stockholm, Jan., 1975.

Vetter, Hermann. "Zur Geschichte der Zentralheizungen bis zum Ubergang in die Neuzeit." *Beitrage zur Geschichte der Technik und Industrie*, No. 3, 1911.

Viherjuuri, H.J. *Sauna: The Finnish Bath*. Stephen Greene Press, Brattleboro, Vt., 1965.

Violett-Le-Duc, E.E. *Dictionnaire Raisonné du Mobilier Francais*. Paris, 1858.

———*The Habitations of Man*. J.R. Osgood, Boston, 1876.

Vitruvius. *The Ten Books on Architecture*. Dover Publications, New York, 1960.

Walbert, Benjamin L. III. "The Infancy of Central Heating in the United States: 1803–1845." *Bulletin of the Association for Preservation Technology*, Vol. III, No. 4. Ottawa, 1971.

Wald, H.-J. "Tawa-Khana in Afghanistan." *Zeitschrift fur Ethnologie*, No. 98. 1973.

Walton, James. "The Skye House." *Antiquity*, Vol. XXXI. 1957.

Weaver, Martin E. "The Cultural Melting Pot in the Kitchen." *Bulletin of the Association for Preservation Technology*, Vol. VIII, No. 1. 1976.

Weiss, Richard. *Hauser und Landschaften der Schweiz.* Eugen Reutsch Verlag, Erlenbach-Zurich, 1959.

Weitz, Charles A. "Weathering Heights." *Natural History,* Vol. 90, No. 11, Nov., 1981.

Wertime, Theodore A., and James D. Muhly. *The Coming of the Age of Iron.* Yale University Press, New Haven, 1980.

Wertime, Theodore A. and Steven F. *Early Pyrotechnology: The Evolution of the First Fire-Using Industries.* Forthcoming.

Winkelmann, Hans. *Wood Burning.* Forestry Occasional Paper No. 1. United Nations, FAO, Rome, 1955.

Wood Energy Institute and Wood Heating Alliance. Proceedings of Seminars I through VIII, 1977 through 1981.

Wright, Lawrence. *Home Fires Burning.* Routledge and Kegan Paul, London, 1964.

Wright, Thomas. *A History of Domestic Manners and Sentiments.* Chapman and Hall, London, 1862.

Wulff, Hans E. *Traditional Crafts of Persia.* M.I.T. Press, Cambridge, Mass., 1966.

Yang, C.K. *Religion in Chinese Society.* University of California Press, Berkeley, 1961.

Youngquist, W.G., and H.O. Fleischer. *Wood in American Life.* Forest Products Research Society, Madison, Wisc., 1977.

ILLUSTRATION CREDITS

Figs. 1, 7, 14, 15 and 53 from Thomas Wright, *A History of Domestic Manners and Sentiments in England During the Middle Ages*. Chapman and Hall, London, 1862.

Figs. 3, 68, 69, 90, 102 and 103 after N. Valonen, *Zur Geschichte der finnischen Wohnstuben*. Suomalais-ugrilainen Seura, Helsinki, 1963. Courtesy of Suomalais-ugrilainen Seura.

Figs. 4, 22, 47, 50 and 128 from Henry Havard, *Dictionnaire de l'ameublement et de la décoration depuis le XIII siècle*. Maison Quantin, Paris, 1887-1890.

Figs. 5, 17, 18, 26, 49, 54 and 55 from Edward S. Morse, *Japanese Homes and Their Surroundings*. Ticknor and Co., Boston 1886.

Fig. 6 Vitruvius Teutsch., Nürnberg, 1548. Spencer Collection, The New York Public Library, Astor, Lenox and Tilden Foundations.

Figs. 8 and 30 from Charles Singer, E. J. Holmyard and A. R. Hall, *A History of Technology*, Vols. I and II. Oxford University Press, London, 1954. Courtesy of Oxford University Press.

Fig. 9 from Dubois de Montpéreux, *Voyage autour du Caucase*. Paris, 1839. Reproduced by permission of The British Library.

Figs. 10, 11 and 12 from Sir Arthur Mitchell, *The Past in the Present*. Harper and Bros., New York, 1881. (Fig. 10 is adapted.)

Fig. 13 from E. E. Viollett-Le-Duc, *The Habitations of Man*. Boston, 1876.

Figs. 16, 37, 46 and 48 from L. A. Shuffrey, *The English Fireplace*. B. T. Batsford, London, 1912. Fig. 19 is adapted from Shuffrey.

Fig. 20, an illustration by Merian from M. Maier, *Atalanta fugiens*, 1618. Courtesy of Deutsches Museum.

Figs. 21, 98, 99, 135, 136, 143 and 170 are photos by Erika Groth-Schmachtenberger.

Fig. 23 after C. Perlès, "Le Feu," *La Prehistoire Française*, Vol. I. Paris, 1976.

Fig. 24 FAO photo by H. A. Wirtz.

Fig. 25 after Walter Cline, *Mining and Metallurgy in Negro Africa*. George Banta Pub. Co., Menasha, Wisc., 1937.

Figs. 27, 38, 41, 42 and 44 courtesy of Frilandsmuseet ved Sorgenfri, Copenhagen.

Fig. 28 from R. J. Forbes, *Studies in Ancient Technology*, Vol. VI. E. J. Brill, Leiden, 1966. Courtesy of E. J. Brill.

Fig. 29 reprinted from *Treatise on Ores and Assaying* by Lazarus Ercker, translated from 1580 Edition by A. G., Sisco and C. S. Smith, by permission of The University of Chicago Press. Copyright © 1951 by University of Chicago Press.

Figs. 31, 56, 57, 95 and 96 from I. Balassa and G. Ortutay, *Magyar Néprajz*. Corvina, Budapest, 1979. Figs. 31, 57 and 95 are photos by Miklós Lantos and Fig. 56 by Szabo Jeno.

Fig. 32 after A. Neuberger, *The Technical Arts and Sciences of the Ancients*. Macmillan, New York, 1930.

Figs. 33, 58, 126, 127, 129, 133, 134, 142 and 160 are photos or drawings made from photos by the author.

Figs. 34, 35 and 43 are adapted or reproduced from P. Kundzins, *Latvju Sēta*. Daugava, Stockholm, 1974. Courtesy of P. Kundzins.

Figs. 36, 131, 140 and 141 from the Blue Book *Deutsche Bauernstuben* by M. Baur-Heinhold, published by Langewiesche-Königstein in Taunus, West Germany, 1975. Courtesy of the publisher.

Fig. 39 an 1808 painting by C. P. Elfstrom, courtesy of Museovirasto, Helsinki.

Fig. 40 from Guiseppe Acerbi, *Travels Through Sweden, Finland and Lapland to the North Cape, 1798-'99*. London, 1802. Courtesy of Museovirasto, Helsinki.

Fig. 45 courtesy of the Estonian State Open Air Museum.

Fig. 51 attributed to the Flemish artist Simon Benninck. From the *Book of Hours*. Reproduced by permission of The British Library.

Fig. 52 after Oliver Rackham, *Trees and Woodland in the British Landscape*. J. M. Dent and Sons Ltd., London, 1976.

Figs. 59, 60, 71, 72, 73 and 77 after Walter Bernan (Robert Meikelham), *On the History and Art of Warming and Ventilating Rooms and Buildings*, 2 vols. George Bell, London, 1845.

Figs. 61 and 86 from Alfred Faber, *1000 Jahre Werdegang von Herd und Ofen*. Deutsches Museum Abhandlungen und Berichte, 18 Jg., 1950, H.3. Courtesy Deutsches Museum.

Figs. 62 and 63 after illustrations in Arne Nygaard-Nilssen, *Norsk Jernskulptur*. J. W. Cappelens Forlag, Oslo, 1944.

Figs. 64 and 65 from the collections of Greenfield Village and the Henry Ford Museum, Dearborn, Mich.

Fig. 66. Photo by Brassai, 1939. Courtesy of the Worcester Art Museum, Worcester, Mass.

Fig. 67 after Tamara Habicht, *Eesti Saun*. Valgus, Tallinn, 1972. Courtesy Copyright Agency of the U.S.S.R.

Fig. 70 after Hans Soeder, *Das Dart Tritschuny im Litavisch*. (Diss.) Berlin-Darmstadt, 1918.

Fig. 74 adapted from a drawing provided by Informationstelle Kachelofen, Stuttgart.

Fig. 75 after H.-J. Wald, *Tawa-Khana in Afghanistan*. Zeitschrift fur Ethnologie, No. 98, 1973.

Figs. 78 and 79 drawings by Edward W. Poitras.

Fig. 80 after Sang-sul Kim, *Ondol Kaejoron*. Seoul, 1961.

Fig. 82 photo by A. F. Kersting, courtesy of The National Trust, London.

Figs. 83, 84, 87, 88 and 89 after H. Vetter, *Zur Geschichte der Zentralheizungen bis zum Ubergang in die Neuzeit*. Beitrage zur Geschichte der Technik und Industrie, No. 3, 1911.

Fig. 85 from the Leiden University Library Collection.

Fig. 91 from *The Weekly Magazine*, Philadelphia, July 21, 1798. Courtesy of The American Philosophical Society.

Fig. 92 after a drawing in Marija Gimbutas, *The Prehistory of Eastern Europe*. The Peabody Museum, Cambridge, Mass., 1956. Courtesy of The Peabody Museum.

Fig. 93 after Z. Bàtky, *Magyar tüzhelyek ès hàztipusok*. Neprajzi Ertesto, Budapest, 1930.

Fig. 94 after a drawing in K. Kwasniewski, *Paleniska i piece w polskim budownictwie ludowym*. Polish Academy of Sciences, Warsaw, 1963.

Fig. 97 after Lajos Kiss, *A Boglyakemence ès èlete Hòdmezövàsàrhelyen*. Ethnographia, Budapest, 1953.

Fig. 100 after a photo by G. M. Rovinskiy, courtesy of the Copyright Agency of the U.S.S.R.

Figs. 104, 105 and 106 after Jaan Jaakson, "Wood Burning Brick Stoves," Reprinted from *Wood Burnng Quarterly*, Fall, 1976 by permission of *Home Energy Digest* and *Wood Burning Quarterly*.

Figs. 107, 108, 109, 112, 173, 174, 175, 176, 177 and 178 from L. A. Semenov, *Teploustojchivost' i pechnoe otoplenie zhilykh i obschestvennykh zdanij*. Ministerstva Stroitelstva Predpryatii Mashinostroenya, Moscow, 1950. Courtesy of the Copyright Agency of the U.S.S.R.

Figs. 110 and 111 after I. S. Podgorodnikov, *Russkaya Pech.* Ministerstva Kommunalnogo Hozyastva Moscow-Leningrad, 1950. Courtesy of the Copyright Agency of the U.S.S.R.

Figs. 113 and 114 after drawings by Bengt Carlén.

Fig. 115 reproduced from documents of the Swedish Academy of Scienc;e, 1739 and 1741.

Figs. 116, 117, 118, 119, 120 and 121 from J. Cronstedt and F. Wrede, *Samling of Beskrifningar pa Atskilliga Eldstader, Inrattade til Besparing af Wede*. Stockholm, 1775.

Fig. 122 from Gosta Selling, "Svenska-1700 Talskakelugnar." *Svenska Kulturbilder*, Stockholm, 1937.

Fig. 123 courtesy of Nordiska Museet.

Fig. 171 courtesy of Rakennustietosäätiö, Helsinki.

Fig. 125 and 172 from G. E. Asp, *Uuninmuuraaja*, Otava, Helsinki, 1944. Courtesy of Otava.

Figs. 130, 137, 138 and 139 from Rosemarie·Franz, *Der Kachelofen*, Akademische Druck-u. Verlagsanstalt, Graz, 1969.

Fig. 132 from A. Jackowski and J. Jarnuskiewicz, *Folk Art of Poland*. Arkady, Warsaw, 1968. Photo by J. Swiderski.

Fig. 144 reprinted from Hassan Fathy, *Architecture for the Poor*. By permission of the University of Chicago Press. Copyright © 1973 by the University of Chicago Press.

Figs. 179 and 180 from H. Grohmann, *Kachelofen und Kamin*. Georg D. W. Callwey, Munich, 1951. Courtesy of the publisher, Georg D. W. Callwey.

Fig. 146 after a drawing provided by Tiba Co., Bubendorf, Switzerland.

Figs. 147, 148 and 149 after drawings by Josef Thurner.

Figs. 153, 154 and 155 after drawings by Alden Krider.

Fig. 156 after a drawing by Don Metz.

Fig. 157 after drawings in *Gilsland Farm Energy System*, copyright 1978 by the Maine Audubon Society. Courtesy of Maine Audubon Society.

Fig. 158 from *Stick Wood Furnace Research at the University of Maine at Orono* by Professor Richard C. Hill. Courtesy of Professor Hill.

Fig. 162 Photo by Nicholas Lyle.

Fig. 163 Courtesy of Thermal Energy Storage Systems, Inc.

Fig. 164 FAO photo by F. Mattioli.

Fig. 165 FAO photo by F. Gonzales de Moya.

Fig. 166 FAO photo by P. Pittet.

Fig. 167 FAO photo.

Figs. 168 and 169 after drawings with an article by J. A. Butler in *The Nebraska Farmer*, June, 1878. Courtesy of the Nebraska Historical Society.

Cover Illustrations Credits

Front: *Top left*—Whitewashed clay stove of a type once common in the Swiss and Austrian Alps. People sat or slept on wooden benches built around the stove or on a platform above it. This model has been reconstructed in the Tiroler Volkskunst Museum in Innsbruck, Austria. Photo by the author. *Bottom left*—Green tile stove from Sweden with a round brass cleanout plug at top center. Photo. courtesy of *Femina*. *Center*—This faience stove, with its built-in seat, dates from 1566 in Switzerland. Photo courtesy of the Swiss National Museum in Zurich. *Right*—This simple brick stove, with a plastered and whitewashed exterior, functions today in a Swedish farmhouse. See Figure 110 for further details. Photo by Bengt Carlén.

Back: Bottom center—This tile stove was built around 1770 in Gleifheim Castle in Austria's South Tyrol. It is fueled via a door on the other side of the wall behind the stove. Photo by Günter von Voithenberg. *Top right*—A brick fireplace/stove built in Canada in 1983. This is a contra-flow model, like that shown in Figure 183. Photo by N. Senf of Masonry Stove Builders, Ottawa, designers and builders of the stove. *Bottom right*—This heat storage fireplace is a completed version of the model whose concrete block core appears in Figure 163. Photo courtesy of Thermal Energy Storage Systems, Inc., of Kenvil, N.J.

188

the politics and practice of sustainable living

CHELSEA GREEN PUBLISHING CO.

CHELSEA GREEN publishes information that helps us lead pleasurable lives on a planet where human activities are in harmony and balance with Nature. Our celebration of the sustainable arts has led us to publish trendsetting books about organic gardening, solar electricity and renewable energy, innovative building techniques, regenerative forestry, local and bioregional democracy, and whole foods. Our works, while intensely practical, are also entertaining and inspirational, demonstrating that an ecological approach to life is consistent with producing beautiful, eloquent, and useful books, and multimedia.

Food

The Slow Food Guide to New York City
Martins and Watson • ISBN 1-931498-27-X
The Slow Food Guide to Chicago
Gibson and Lowndes • ISBN 1-931498-61-X
$20.00 each

Planet

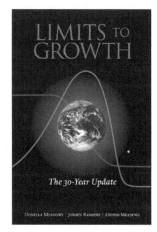

Limits to Growth: The 30-Year Update
Donella Meadows, Jorgen Randers,
and Dennis Meadows
ISBN 1-931498-58-X • $22.50

Shelter

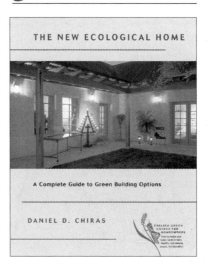

The New Ecological Home: A Complete Guide to Green Building Options
Daniel D. Chiras
ISBN 1-931498-16-4 • $35.00

People

This Organic Life: Confessions of a Suburban Homesteader
Joan Dye Gussow
ISBN 1-931498-24-5 • $16.95